TEACHER'S GUIDE

Connected Mathematics 2™

Bits and Pieces II

Using Fraction Operations

Glenda Lappan
James T. Fey
William M. Fitzgerald
Susan N. Friel
Elizabeth Difanis Phillips

PEARSON

Boston, Massachusetts · Glenview, Illinois · Shoreview, Minnesota · Upper Saddle River, New Jersey

Connected Mathematics™ was developed at Michigan State University with financial support from the Michigan State University Office of the Provost, Computing and Technology, and the College of Natural Science.

This material is based upon work supported by the National Science Foundation under Grant No. MDR 9150217 and Grant No. ESI 9986372. Opinions expressed are those of the authors and not necessarily those of the Foundation.

The Michigan State University authors and administration have agreed that all MSU royalties arising from this publication will be devoted to purposes supported by the Department of Mathematics and the MSU Mathematics Enrichment Fund.

13-digit ISBN 978-0-13-366185-9
10-digit ISBN 0-13-366185-7
2 3 4 5 6 7 8 9 10   11 10 09 08

Authors of Connected Mathematics

(from left to right) Glenda Lappan, Betty Phillips, Susan Friel, Bill Fitzgerald, Jim Fey

Glenda Lappan is a University Distinguished Professor in the Department of Mathematics at Michigan State University. Her research and development interests are in the connected areas of students' learning of mathematics and mathematics teachers' professional growth and change related to the development and enactment of K–12 curriculum materials.

James T. Fey is a Professor of Curriculum and Instruction and Mathematics at the University of Maryland. His consistent professional interest has been development and research focused on curriculum materials that engage middle and high school students in problem-based collaborative investigations of mathematical ideas and their applications.

William M. Fitzgerald (*Deceased*) was a Professor in the Department of Mathematics at Michigan State University. His early research was on the use of concrete materials in supporting student learning and led to the development of teaching materials for laboratory environments. Later he helped develop a teaching model to support student experimentation with mathematics.

Susan N. Friel is a Professor of Mathematics Education in the School of Education at the University of North Carolina at Chapel Hill. Her research interests focus on statistics education for middle-grade students and, more broadly, on teachers' professional development and growth in teaching mathematics K–8.

Elizabeth Difanis Phillips is a Senior Academic Specialist in the Mathematics Department of Michigan State University. She is interested in teaching and learning mathematics for both teachers and students. These interests have led to curriculum and professional development projects at the middle school and high school levels, as well as projects related to the teaching and learning of algebra across the grades.

Field Test Sites for CMP2

During the development of the revised edition of *Connected Mathematics* (CMP2), more than 100 classroom teachers have field-tested materials at 49 school sites in 12 states and the District of Columbia. This classroom testing occurred over three academic years (2001 through 2004), allowing careful study of the effectiveness of each of the 24 units that comprise the program. A special thanks to the students and teachers at these pilot schools.

Arkansas
Magnolia Public Schools
Kittena Bell*, Judith Trowell*; *Central Elementary School:* Maxine Broom, Betty Eddy, Tiffany Fallin, Bonnie Flurry, Carolyn Monk, Elizabeth Tye; *Magnolia Junior High School:* Monique Bryan, Ginger Cook, David Graham, Shelby Lamkin

Colorado
Boulder Public Schools
Nevin Platt Middle School: Judith Koenig

St. Vrain Valley School District, Longmont
Westview Middle School: Colleen Beyer, Kitty Canupp, Ellie Decker*, Peggy McCarthy, Tanya deNobrega, Cindy Payne, Ericka Pilon, Andrew Roberts

District of Columbia
Capitol Hill Day School: Ann Lawrence

Georgia
University of Georgia, Athens
Brad Findell

Madison Public Schools
Morgan County Middle School: Renee Burgdorf, Lynn Harris, Nancy Kurtz, Carolyn Stewart

Maine
Falmouth Public Schools
Falmouth Middle School: Donna Erikson, Joyce Hebert, Paula Hodgkins, Rick Hogan, David Legere, Cynthia Martin, Barbara Stiles, Shawn Towle*

Michigan
Portland Public Schools
Portland Middle School: Mark Braun, Holly DeRosia, Kathy Dole*, Angie Foote, Teri Keusch, Tammi Wardwell

Traverse City Area Public Schools
Bertha Vos Elementary: Kristin Sak; *Central Grade School:* Michelle Clark; Jody Meyers; *Eastern Elementary:* Karrie Tufts; *Interlochen Elementary:* Mary McGee-Cullen; *Long Lake Elementary:* Julie Faulkner*, Charlie Maxbauer, Katherine Sleder; *Norris Elementary:* Hope Slanaker; *Oak Park Elementary:* Jessica Steed; *Traverse Heights Elementary:* Jennifer Wolfert; *Westwoods Elementary:* Nancy Conn; *Old Mission Peninsula School:* Deb Larimer; *Traverse City East Junior High:* Ivanka Berkshire, Ruthanne Kladder, Jan Palkowski, Jane Peterson, Mary Beth Schmitt; *Traverse City West Junior High:* Dan Fouch*, Ray Fouch

Sturgis Public Schools
Sturgis Middle School: Ellen Eisele

Minnesota
Burnsville School District 191
Hidden Valley Elementary: Stephanie Cin, Jane McDevitt

Hopkins School District 270
Alice Smith Elementary: Sandra Cowing, Kathleen Gustafson, Martha Mason, Scott Stillman; *Eisenhower Elementary:* Chad Bellig, Patrick Berger, Nancy Glades, Kye Johnson, Shane Wasserman, Victoria Wilson; *Gatewood Elementary:* Sarah Ham, Julie Kloos, Janine Pung, Larry Wade; *Glen Lake Elementary:* Jacqueline Cramer, Kathy Hering, Cecelia Morris, Robb Trenda; *Katherine Curren Elementary:* Diane Bancroft, Sue DeWit, John Wilson; *L. H. Tanglen Elementary:* Kevin Athmann, Lisa Becker, Mary LaBelle, Kathy Rezac, Roberta Severson; *Meadowbrook Elementary:* Jan Gauger, Hildy Shank, Jessica Zimmerman; *North Junior High:* Laurel Hahn, Kristin Lee, Jodi Markuson, Bruce Mestemacher, Laurel Miller, Bonnie Rinker, Jeannine Salzer, Sarah Shafer, Cam Stottler; *West Junior High:* Alicia Beebe, Kristie Earl, Nobu Fujii, Pam Georgetti, Susan Gilbert, Regina Nelson Johnson, Debra Lindstrom, Michele Luke*, Jon Sorensen

Minneapolis School District 1
Ann Sullivan K–8 School: Bronwyn Collins; Anne Bartel* (Curriculum and Instruction Office)

Wayzata School District 284
Central Middle School: Sarajane Myers, Dan Nielsen, Tanya Ravnholdt

White Bear Lake School District 624
Central Middle School: Amy Jorgenson, Michelle Reich, Brenda Sammon

New York
New York City Public Schools
IS 89: Yelena Aynbinder, Chi-Man Ng, Nina Rapaport, Joel Spengler, Phyllis Tam*, Brent Wyso; *Wagner Middle School:* Jason Appel, Intissar Fernandez, Yee Gee Get, Richard Goldstein, Irving Marcus, Sue Norton, Bernadita Owens, Jennifer Rehn*, Kevin Yuhas

---

* indicates a Field Test Site Coordinator

Ohio

Talawanda School District, Oxford
Talawanda Middle School: Teresa Abrams, Larry Brock, Heather Brosey, Julie Churchman, Monna Even, Karen Fitch, Bob George, Amanda Klee, Pat Meade, Sandy Montgomery, Barbara Sherman, Lauren Steidl

Miami University
Jeffrey Wanko*

Springfield Public Schools
Rockway School: Jim Mamer

Pennsylvania

Pittsburgh Public Schools
Kenneth Labuskes, Marianne O'Connor, Mary Lynn Raith*; *Arthur J. Rooney Middle School:* David Hairston, Stamatina Mousetis, Alfredo Zangaro; *Frick International Studies Academy:* Suzanne Berry, Janet Falkowski, Constance Finseth, Romika Hodge, Frank Machi; *Reizenstein Middle School:* Jeff Baldwin, James Brautigam, Lorena Burnett, Glen Cobbett, Michael Jordan, Margaret Lazur, Tamar McPherson, Melissa Munnell, Holly Neely, Ingrid Reed, Dennis Reft

Texas

Austin Independent School District
Bedichek Middle School: Lisa Brown, Jennifer Glasscock, Vicki Massey

El Paso Independent School District
Cordova Middle School: Armando Aguirre, Anneliesa Durkes, Sylvia Guzman, Pat Holguin*, William Holguin, Nancy Nava, Laura Orozco, Michelle Peña, Roberta Rosen, Patsy Smith, Jeremy Wolf

Plano Independent School District
Patt Henry, James Wohlgehagen*; *Frankford Middle School:* Mandy Baker, Cheryl Butsch, Amy Dudley, Betsy Eshelman, Janet Greene, Cort Haynes, Kathy Letchworth, Kay Marshall, Kelly McCants, Amy Reck, Judy Scott, Syndy Snyder, Lisa Wang; *Wilson Middle School:* Darcie Bane, Amanda Bedenko, Whitney Evans, Tonelli Hatley, Sarah (Becky) Higgs, Kelly Johnston, Rebecca McElligott, Kay Neuse, Cheri Slocum, Kelli Straight

Washington

Evergreen School District
Shahala Middle School: Nicole Abrahamsen, Terry Coon*, Carey Doyle, Sheryl Drechsler, George Gemma, Gina Helland, Amy Hilario, Darla Lidyard, Sean McCarthy, Tilly Meyer, Willow Nuewelt, Todd Parsons, Brian Pederson, Stan Posey, Shawn Scott, Craig Sjoberg, Lynette Sundstrom, Charles Switzer, Luke Youngblood

Wisconsin

Beaver Dam Unified School District
Beaver Dam Middle School: Jim Braemer, Jeanne Frick, Jessica Greatens, Barbara Link, Dennis McCormick, Karen Michels, Nancy Nichols*, Nancy Palm, Shelly Stelsel, Susan Wiggins

---

* indicates a Field Test Site Coordinator

Reviews of CMP to Guide Development of CMP2

Before writing for CMP2 began or field tests were conducted, the first edition of *Connected Mathematics* was submitted to the mathematics faculties of school districts from many parts of the country and to 80 individual reviewers for extensive comments.

School District Survey Reviews of CMP

Arizona
Madison School District #38 (Phoenix)

Arkansas
Cabot School District, Little Rock School District, Magnolia School District

California
Los Angeles Unified School District

Colorado
St. Vrain Valley School District (Longmont)

Florida
Leon County Schools (Tallahassee)

Illinois
School District #21 (Wheeling)

Indiana
Joseph L. Block Junior High (East Chicago)

Kentucky
Fayette County Public Schools (Lexington)

Maine
Selection of Schools

Massachusetts
Selection of Schools

Michigan
Sparta Area Schools

Minnesota
Hopkins School District

Texas
Austin Independent School District, The El Paso Collaborative for Academic Excellence, Plano Independent School District

Wisconsin
Platteville Middle School

Individual Reviewers of CMP

Arkansas
Deborah Cramer; Robby Frizzell *(Taylor)*; Lowell Lynde *(University of Arkansas, Monticello)*; Leigh Manzer *(Norfork)*; Lynne Roberts *(Emerson High School, Emerson)*; Tony Timms *(Cabot Public Schools)*; Judith Trowell *(Arkansas Department of Higher Education)*

California
José Alcantar *(Gilroy)*; Eugenie Belcher *(Gilroy)*; Marian Pasternack *(Lowman M. S. T. Center, North Hollywood)*; Susana Pezoa *(San Jose)*; Todd Rabusin *(Hollister)*; Margaret Siegfried *(Ocala Middle School, San Jose)*; Polly Underwood *(Ocala Middle School, San Jose)*

Colorado
Janeane Golliher *(St. Vrain Valley School District, Longmont)*; Judith Koenig *(Nevin Platt Middle School, Boulder)*

Florida
Paige Loggins *(Swift Creek Middle School, Tallahassee)*

Illinois
Jan Robinson *(School District #21, Wheeling)*

Indiana
Frances Jackson *(Joseph L. Block Junior High, East Chicago)*

Kentucky
Natalee Feese *(Fayette County Public Schools, Lexington)*

Maine
Betsy Berry *(Maine Math & Science Alliance, Augusta)*

Maryland
Joseph Gagnon *(University of Maryland, College Park)*; Paula Maccini *(University of Maryland, College Park)*

Massachusetts
George Cobb *(Mt. Holyoke College, South Hadley)*; Cliff Kanold *(University of Massachusetts, Amherst)*

Michigan
Mary Bouck *(Farwell Area Schools)*; Carol Dorer *(Slauson Middle School, Ann Arbor)*; Carrie Heaney *(Forsythe Middle School, Ann Arbor)*; Ellen Hopkins *(Clague Middle School, Ann Arbor)*; Teri Keusch *(Portland Middle School, Portland)*; Valerie Mills *(Oakland Schools, Waterford)*; Mary Beth Schmitt *(Traverse City East Junior High, Traverse City)*; Jack Smith *(Michigan State University, East Lansing)*; Rebecca Spencer *(Sparta Middle School, Sparta)*; Ann Marie Nicoll Turner *(Tappan Middle School, Ann Arbor)*; Scott Turner *(Scarlett Middle School, Ann Arbor)*

Minnesota
Margarita Alvarez *(Olson Middle School, Minneapolis)*; Jane Amundson *(Nicollet Junior High, Burnsville)*; Anne Bartel *(Minneapolis Public Schools)*; Gwen Ranzau Campbell *(Sunrise Park Middle School, White Bear Lake)*; Stephanie Cin *(Hidden Valley Elementary, Burnsville)*; Joan Garfield *(University of Minnesota, Minneapolis)*; Gretchen Hall *(Richfield Middle School, Richfield)*; Jennifer Larson *(Olson Middle School, Minneapolis)*; Michele Luke *(West Junior High, Minnetonka)*; Jeni Meyer *(Richfield Junior High, Richfield)*; Judy Pfingsten *(Inver Grove Heights Middle School, Inver Grove Heights)*; Sarah Shafer *(North Junior High, Minnetonka)*; Genni Steele *(Central Middle School, White Bear Lake)*; Victoria Wilson *(Eisenhower Elementary, Hopkins)*; Paul Zorn *(St. Olaf College, Northfield)*

New York
Debra Altenau-Bartolino *(Greenwich Village Middle School, New York)*; Doug Clements *(University of Buffalo)*; Francis Curcio *(New York University, New York)*; Christine Dorosh *(Clinton School for Writers, Brooklyn)*; Jennifer Rehn *(East Side Middle School, New York)*; Phyllis Tam *(IS 89 Lab School, New York)*;

Marie Turini *(Louis Armstrong Middle School, New York)*; Lucy West *(Community School District 2, New York)*; Monica Witt *(Simon Baruch Intermediate School 104, New York)*

Pennsylvania
Robert Aglietti *(Pittsburgh)*; Sharon Mihalich *(Freeport)*; Jennifer Plumb *(South Hills Middle School, Pittsburgh)*; Mary Lynn Raith *(Pittsburgh Public Schools)*

Texas
Michelle Bittick *(Austin Independent School District)*; Margaret Cregg *(Plano Independent School District)*; Sheila Cunningham *(Klein Independent School District)*; Judy Hill *(Austin Independent School District)*; Patricia Holguin *(El Paso Independent School District)*; Bonnie McNemar *(Arlington)*; Kay Neuse *(Plano Independent School District)*; Joyce Polanco *(Austin Independent School District)*; Marge Ramirez *(University of Texas at El Paso)*; Pat Rossman *(Baker Campus, Austin)*; Cindy Schimek *(Houston)*; Cynthia Schneider *(Charles A. Dana Center, University of Texas at Austin)*; Uri Treisman *(Charles A. Dana Center, University of Texas at Austin)*; Jacqueline Weilmuenster *(Grapevine-Colleyville Independent School District)*; LuAnn Weynand *(San Antonio)*; Carmen Whitman *(Austin Independent School District)*; James Wohlgehagen *(Plano Independent School District)*

Washington
Ramesh Gangolli *(University of Washington, Seattle)*

Wisconsin
Susan Lamon *(Marquette University, Hales Corner)*; Steve Reinhart *(retired, Chippewa Falls Middle School, Eau Claire)*

Bits and Pieces II
Understanding Fraction Operations

The Student Edition pages for the Unit Opener follow page 18.

Bits and Pieces II
Understanding Fraction Operations

Goals of the Unit

- Use benchmarks and other strategies to estimate the reasonableness of results of operations with fractions

- Develop ways to model sums, differences, products, and quotients with areas, strips, and number lines

- Use estimates and exact solutions to make decisions

- Look for and generalize patterns in numbers

- Use knowledge of fractions and equivalence of fractions to develop algorithms for adding, subtracting, multiplying, and dividing fractions

- Recognize when addition, subtraction, multiplication, or division is the appropriate operation to solve a problem

- Write fact families to show the inverse relationship between addition and subtraction, and between multiplication and division

- Solve problems using arithmetic operations on fractions

Developing Students' Mathematical Habits

The overall goal of *Connected Mathematics* is to help students develop sound mathematical habits. Through their work in this and other number units, students learn important questions to ask themselves about any situation that is represented and modeled mathematically, such as:

- *What kinds of models can be used to show computation with fractions?*

- *Will the strategies and algorithms we have developed apply to all fractional quantities?*

- *What do whole number operations reveal about the meaning of operations with fractions?*

- *Do results from algorithms support those found with the models?*

- *How can estimation help in this situation?*

Overview

The overall goal of *Bits and Pieces II* is to develop meaning for and skill with computations involving fractions. When students finish this unit they should know algorithms for computations that they understand and can use with ease. This unit does not teach a specific or preferred algorithm for working with rational numbers. Instead it helps the teacher create a classroom environment in which students work on problems and generate ideas and strategies that make sense to them. At a point in the development of each operation, students are asked to pull together their strategies into an algorithm that works for all fraction situations involving that operation. As they work individually, in groups, and as a whole class on the problems, they develop and practice the algorithms to develop skill in carrying them out. This development process allows students to recognize special cases that can be easily handled and yet ends with students having an efficient general algorithm that works for all cases within an operation.

Letting the students wrestle with making sense of situations may take more time in the beginning. However, the payoff in the long run is that students learn to think and to reason about mathematical situations and although the algorithms need practice, they will not need to be taught repeatedly. The invented algorithms of students are often efficient and can evolve into standard algorithms. As they do, students understand why standard algorithms work.

We expect that when students finish this unit they will have an understanding of the meaning for computations with fractions. Students should be able to decide which operation is appropriate in a given situation. In addition, students should be able to use number sense, benchmarks, and operation sense to estimate solutions for computational situations as well as use estimation to decide if exact answers are reasonable.

Summary of Investigations

Investigation 1

Estimating With Fractions

Investigation 1 focuses on estimating sums of fractions and decimals. It builds on work with benchmarks, ordering, and the relationship between decimals and fractions in *Bits and Pieces I*. Students play a game in which they estimate the size of sums. Students also explore underestimation and overestimation as a strategy to reason about contextual situations where an estimate is needed and it is important to know if the estimate is above or below an exact amount.

Investigation 2

Adding and Subtracting Fractions

This investigation focuses on developing computational understanding and skill in adding and subtracting fractions. This investigation does not *give* students algorithms for computation. Instead, it prepares students to figure out how to add and subtract fractions by emphasizing flexibility in finding equivalent fractions. In the course of solving the problems, students develop strategies for adding and subtracting fractions and mixed numbers. Through class discussion these strategies are made more explicit and efficient. The inverse relationship between addition and subtraction is developed through the exploration of fact families. Although many students understand that addition and subtraction are related in whole-number contexts, they do not always extend this idea to include fractions. The last problem gives students presorted addition and subtraction problems to solve, characterize, and from which to create a general algorithm.

Investigation 3
Multiplying With Fractions

Investigation 3 focuses on developing computational skill with and understanding of fraction multiplication. Various contexts and models are introduced to help students make sense of when multiplication is appropriate. The first two problems develop multiplication with simple fractions and the third and fourth problems focus on fraction, mixed number, and whole number combinations. Estimation is developed across the problems in the investigation, as well as the idea that multiplication does not always lead to a larger product. The last problem is structured like the one used to develop addition and subtraction algorithms. Students are given a set of presorted multiplication problems. Through the process of solving and characterizing how the problems are categorized, students develop a general algorithm for fraction multiplication.

Investigation 4
Dividing With Fractions

This investigation has the same goals as Investigations 2 and 3, except the operation of division is explored. Everyday situations are used to help students make sense of when division is an appropriate operation. The inverse relationship of multiplication and division is explored. The last problem uses presorted division problems to develop a general algorithm for fraction division.

Mathematics Background

Writing Number Sentences

Helping students learn to use mathematical language (i.e., symbols) correctly and with confidence is a goal of the CMP materials. We do this by using symbols connected to contexts so that the context gives the symbols meaning. Using symbolic notation, as well as reformulating symbolic expressions using the rules and syntax of mathematics, can give new insights into problem situations. These are among the fundamental activities of mathematics. Learning the symbolic language of mathematics requires experience to make sense of what the symbols mean and how to operate with them. In CMP, we develop symbolic proficiency over time. You will see students

frequently asked to write a number sentence to capture their work. The sentences become more symbolic in grade seven and reach higher levels of sophistication in grade eight units.

Developing Algorithms

Rational numbers are the heart of the middle-grade experiences with number concepts. The concepts of fractions and operations on fractions can be difficult for students. Part of the reason for students' confusion about rational numbers can be a rush to symbol manipulation with fraction operations without time spent in making sense of the concepts and building experiences that show reasons for why the algorithms work. In addition, students need to understand the operations in ways that help them to judge what operation or combination of operations is needed in a given situation. This unit is designed to provide experiences in building algorithms for the four basic operations with fractions, as well as opportunities for students to consider when such operations are useful in solving problems. Building this kind of thinking and reasoning supports the development of skill with the algorithms. By the end of this unit, we expect students to have efficient algorithms for all four basic operations with fractions, including mixed numbers.

The development of algorithms in this unit draws upon concepts and procedures developed in *Bits and Pieces I*. In *Bits and Pieces I*, students developed an understanding of basic interpretations, models, equivalence, and ordering of rational numbers. In *Bits and Pieces II*, we draw upon this development and the models that were introduced—fraction strips or bars, number lines, grid-area, and partition models—because they connect directly to operations on rational numbers. See *Mathematics Background* in the Teacher's Guide of *Bits and Pieces I* for a full discussion of the concepts and models introduced.

For all four operations we use the same type of development. The development of algorithms for each operation and the understanding of those algorithms involve experiences with contextual problems, models, strategies, and estimation. Problems in context help students make sense of an operation and how the operation can be computed. The problem contexts lead students to model situations and to write number sentences that are representative of the particular situation so they begin to make sense of when an operation is appropriate. Students are often asked to make estimates and use them to decide if their models and symbolic work are reasonable. By analyzing the diagrams and models they develop and their resulting quantities, and relating this to their symbolic work and their estimates, students begin to develop algorithms for fraction operations. An underlying goal of all this work is learning to both write and read mathematical language.

For each operation, the last problem in the investigation asks students to analyze a set of sorted computation problems that seem to belong together. They compute the problems and then look for strategies that can be used in a case of that sort. These are refined into algorithms that are efficient for all cases. Usually the students end up with algorithms that are like the standard algorithms taught by direct instruction in many programs. But, they also end up with understanding and insight into the operations and when they are useful. Also, students will have useful strategies for computations with particular number situations. For example, students may come to realize that in a multiplication problem if one factor is $\frac{1}{2}$, you can compute the product by doubling the denominator of the other factor because the piece size needs to be half as big. $\frac{3}{8} \times \frac{1}{2} = \frac{3}{16}$.

Estimation

Rather than rush to compute in a given situation, students have experiences with estimating sums, differences, products, and quotients. The initial questions CMP helps students to ask are, "About how big will the answer be? What answer makes sense?" These give students a way to know if their computations are wrong, whether the calculation has been done by hand or by calculator. Developing such a sense of fractions and operations takes a long time. At this point in the curriculum students have had quite a bit of practice finding equivalent fractions and decimals and changing among fractions. They have developed some benchmark fractions that they can use to estimate relative size. Students will use these skills to develop strategies to estimate fraction computations.

The strategies used to estimate can differ. For example, in a situation where the goal is to decide what whole number a sum is closest to or what is

a reasonable sum, a useful strategy is to round the numbers to the nearest benchmark. In contrast, you may want to use an estimation strategy that leads to an estimate that you know is too large (overestimate) or too small (underestimate). Consider the situation where you go shopping and you cannot spend more than $20. When you estimate the total cost of the items you want to purchase, you need to estimate in such a way that you can be sure your actual sum is less than $20. Using a purposeful estimation approach, in this case an overestimate, you can know whether or not your actual sum will be less than $20.

Addition and Subtraction

Strategies for operations with fractions can be developed with contexts that help students learn how to put fractions together and take them apart. As students model and symbolize aspects of contextual situations, students develop meaning for and skill in using the operations of addition and subtraction. Additionally, students learn the value of equivalence when changing the representation of fractions to a form with common denominators so that the numerators can be added or subtracted.

Students' previous work with equivalence and partitioning is critical to the development of strategies for adding or subtracting. The following area model provides a context where both naming fractional parts of a whole and equivalence can emerge as students try to write number sentences to model combining section A with section B.

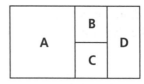

In order to find the sum of A + B, or $\frac{1}{2} + \frac{1}{8}$, students need to use equivalent fractions to rename $\frac{1}{2}$ as $\frac{4}{8}$. The area model helps students visualize A, $\frac{1}{2}$, as 4 eighth-sized sections. By asking students to write number sentences, and to explain how the number sentence helped them arrived at the sum $\frac{5}{8}$, students begin to understand why it is necessary to rename fractions when adding and subtracting and the role that equivalence plays in doing so.

In addition to equivalent fractions, students will need to draw on their understanding of equivalent forms. In *Bits and Pieces I* students worked with the relationship between a mixed number and an improper fraction. As students develop strategies to add and subtract fractions in situations that lead to borrowing or carrying, students learn the value of being able to rewrite fractions in equivalent forms. For example, understanding why $8\frac{2}{3}$ is equivalent to $7\frac{5}{3}$ is critical to understanding how to borrow in fraction situations.

There are other models that can be used to highlight the role of equivalence and support understanding of addition and subtraction. The *fraction-strip model* was used in conjunction with the *number-line model* in *Bits and Pieces I* to develop meaning for fractions and equivalence. Here fraction strips are used to represent $\frac{1}{2} + \frac{1}{3} = \frac{5}{6}$.

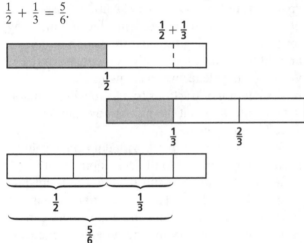

The *number-line model* helps make the connection to fractions as numbers or quantities. This is a number line for 0 to 2 marked to illustrate $1\frac{1}{3} - \frac{2}{3} = \frac{2}{3}$.

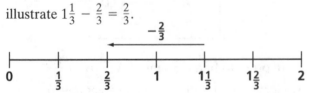

Multiplication

One of the first hurdles for students in their understanding of multiplication of fractions is realizing that multiplication does not always "make larger," as their experience with whole number multiplication has firmly established. In fact, with multiplication of a fraction by a whole number, the fraction can be interpreted as *an operator* that may "stretch" (make larger) or "shrink" (make smaller) depending on whether the fraction is greater or less than 1. This is a big idea that supports understanding what multiplication of fractions entails.

A second hurdle for students is understanding that when they encounter a situation where one needs to take a fraction *of* a quantity, *of* means multiplication. For example, to find $\frac{2}{3}$ of 9, you multiply $\frac{2}{3} \times 9$ to get 6. The temptation is very great to start by telling students this rather than have them encounter the dilemma of the meaning of *of*. In resolving what *of* means in this context, student learning is enhanced.

Models for multiplication of fractions used in the unit are both area models and partitioning. Area models are also useful to help students represent situations, especially multiplication and later decimals and percents. The diagram shows $\frac{4}{5}$ of $\frac{1}{3}$.

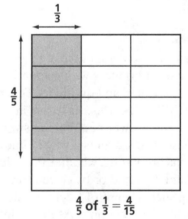

$$\frac{4}{5} \text{ of } \frac{1}{3} = \frac{4}{15}$$

Students also use a model of fraction situations that is based on *partitioning* a number line or strip. The example shows finding $\frac{4}{5}$ of $\frac{1}{3}$ or $\frac{4}{5} \times \frac{1}{3}$. (Figure 1)

You may see students use discrete models to make sense of situations where they are working on discrete objects. An example of a discrete situation is finding $\frac{3}{4}$ of 16 apples. Here each apple represents a separate entity.

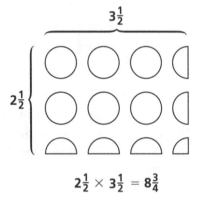

$\frac{3}{4}$ of 16 = 12

Another example, below, shows $2\frac{1}{2} \times 3\frac{1}{2}$.

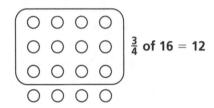

$2\frac{1}{2} \times 3\frac{1}{2} = 8\frac{3}{4}$

Developing the Multiplication Algorithm

Students notice that multiplication is easy for proper fractions because they can just multiply the numerators and multiply the denominators.

However, they have little understanding of why this works. The models we have discussed can help you support understanding. The following looks at both the area and the number-line model as a means of understanding why the algorithm works.

Consider the problem $\frac{2}{3} \times \frac{3}{4}$. To show $\frac{2}{3} \times \frac{3}{4}$ with an area model, first represent the $\frac{3}{4}$ by dividing a square into fourths and shading three of the fourths.

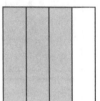

To represent taking $\frac{2}{3}$ of $\frac{3}{4}$, divide the whole into thirds by cutting the square the opposite way, then shade two of the three sections. The part where the shaded sections overlap represents the product, $\frac{6}{12}$.

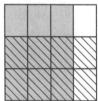

Note what happens to the numerator and the denominator when you partition and how this is related to the algorithm for multiplying fractions. When the square is partitioned, the denominators are used to partition and repartition the whole. In this problem, there are fourths or four parts. When the fourths are partitioned into thirds, or three parts each, the number of pieces in the

Figure 1

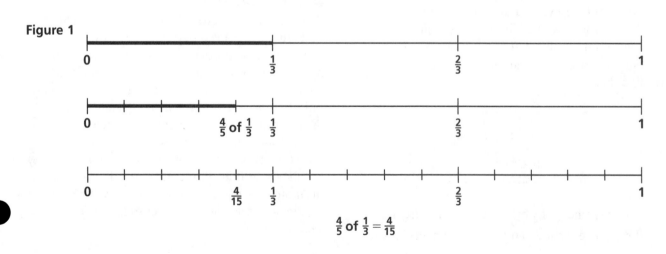

$\frac{4}{5}$ of $\frac{1}{3} = \frac{4}{15}$

whole triples so there are 12 pieces. In the algorithm, when you multiply the denominators (3×4), you are resizing the whole to have the correct number of parts. This means that the denominator in the product has the same role as the denominator in a single fraction. The role is to determine how many parts are in the whole.

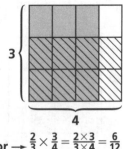

denominator → $\frac{2}{3} \times \frac{3}{4} = \frac{2 \times 3}{3 \times 4} = \frac{6}{12}$

Likewise, the numerator is keeping track of how many of the one-twelfth parts are being referenced. During the original partitioning, $\frac{3}{4}$, or 3 fourth-sized parts, were shaded. In order to take $\frac{2}{3}$ of the 3 one-fourth sized parts, you have to take 2 of the one-twelfth sections from each of the 3 one-fourth sized parts. This can be represented by the product of the numerators 2×3.

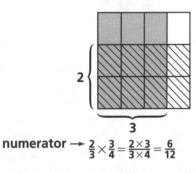

numerator → $\frac{2}{3} \times \frac{3}{4} = \frac{2 \times 3}{3 \times 4} = \frac{6}{12}$

Note that dividing a square with both horizontal and vertical lines for the first fraction does not lead to the kind of partitioning that suggests multiplication of numerators and denominators. For example, if you represent $\frac{3}{4}$ like this:

you may find $\frac{2}{3}$ of $\frac{3}{4}$ by noticing that there are three pieces shaded and you are concerned with

2 of them, so the answer is $\frac{2}{4}$. This is a perfectly reasonable strategy for this problem. The question is whether this strategy will *always* work no matter what fractions. For $\frac{1}{5} \times \frac{2}{3}$ this is not a helpful strategy.

The following illustrates how the *number-line model* is helpful for $\frac{1}{5} \times \frac{2}{3} = \frac{2}{15}$ and is generalizable, even if tedious with large numerators or denominators.

Draw a number line and label 0 and 1. Partition the number line into thirds and mark $\frac{1}{3}$ and $\frac{2}{3}$.

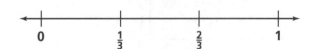

Now break each third into 5 equal parts to get a total of 15 equal parts.

Each fifth of a third is $\frac{1}{15}$, so the two parts marked would be $\frac{2}{15}$. Again the product of the numerators gives the numerator of the product and the product of the denominators gives the denominator of the product.

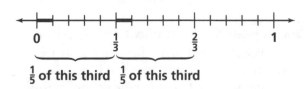

$\frac{1}{5}$ of this third $\frac{1}{5}$ of this third

Using Distribution as a Strategy to Multiply Fractions

Another approach to multiplication of fractions that students use is based on the distributive property. This approach is often used when mixed numbers are involved. Many students use the ideas of breaking a number apart quite intuitively, but often do so incorrectly. The terminology of distribution is not important for students to know at this time. However, because students often use this strategy incorrectly, we provide an opportunity to talk about it in Problem 3.4. We do not wish to promote it as the only approach to multiplying fractions, but as one that is sensible in some situations.

Here is an algorithm for whole number multiplication that uses this approach. Consider the problem 32×24.

$$
\begin{array}{r}
32 \\
\times\ 24 \\
\hline
8 \leftarrow 4 \times 2 \\
120 \leftarrow 4 \times 30 \\
40 \leftarrow 20 \times 2 \\
600 \leftarrow 20 \times 30 \\
\hline
768
\end{array}
$$

This approach is very much like multiplying binomials in algebra. It involves breaking up both numbers into their respective tens and ones. With 32×24 it looks like this:

$$30 \times 20 = 600 \qquad\qquad 2 \times 20 = 40$$
$$(30 + 2) \times (20 + 4) \qquad (30 + 2) \times (20 + 4)$$
$$30 \times 4 = 120 \qquad\qquad 2 \times 4 = 8$$

First, multiply 30 times 20 (tens place in 24) and then 30 times 4 (ones place in 24). Next, multiply by the 2 in the ones place of 32. Multiply 2 times 20 (tens place in 24) followed by 2 times 4 (ones place in 24). Finally, total each partial product $(600 + 120 + 40 + 8)$ to arrive at a total product of 768.

With a problem like $2\frac{1}{2} \times 2\frac{1}{4}$, students may break up each factor and try to work with $(2 + \frac{1}{2}) \times (2 + \frac{1}{4})$. If they distribute correctly, they would reason as shown next.

$$2 \times 2 = 4$$
$$(2 + \tfrac{1}{2}) \times (2 + \tfrac{1}{4})$$
$$2 \times \tfrac{1}{4} = \tfrac{1}{2}$$
and
$$\tfrac{1}{2} \times 2 = 1$$
$$(2 + \tfrac{1}{2}) \times (2 + \tfrac{1}{4}) \quad \rightarrow \quad 4 + \tfrac{1}{2} + 1 + \tfrac{1}{8} = 5\tfrac{5}{8}$$
$$\tfrac{1}{2} \times \tfrac{1}{4} = \tfrac{1}{8}$$

Another approach that makes sense with this problem is to work with $(2 + \frac{1}{2}) \times 2\frac{1}{4}$. If you only break up the first factor the reasoning is as follows:

$$2 \times 2\tfrac{1}{4} = 4\tfrac{1}{2}$$
$$(2 + \tfrac{1}{2}) \times 2\tfrac{1}{4} \quad \rightarrow \quad 4\tfrac{1}{2} + 1\tfrac{1}{8} = 5\tfrac{5}{8}$$
$$\tfrac{1}{2} \times 2\tfrac{1}{4} = 1\tfrac{1}{8}$$

Division

Division also has its share of conceptual difficulties. The answer to a division involving fractions is not necessarily smaller than the dividend. Again it depends on the size of the fraction for both the dividend and the divisor. For example, $3 \div \frac{1}{3} = 9$ and $\frac{1}{4} \div \frac{1}{3} = \frac{3}{4}$ result in a quotient that is larger than the dividend or the divisor. However, in $\frac{1}{3} \div 9 = \frac{1}{27}$, the quotient is smaller than either the dividend or the divisor, and in $\frac{1}{4} \div \frac{3}{4} = \frac{1}{3}$, the quotient is between the dividend and the divisor! Examination of division of fractions in context can help students build an understanding of the operation as well as skill in predicting (or estimating) the kind of answer expected.

In the development of meaning of operations, we ask students to write problems that fit a given computation expression. This will tell you a lot about whether students can interpret different kinds of division situations and whether they can make sense of what the answer to a division problem, including its fractional part, means in a given situation.

In order for students to make sense of any division algorithm, they need to think about what the problem is asking. Creating diagrams to model division problems is a key part of developing this understanding. There are cases where the use of pictorial reasoning is more efficient or just as efficient as an algorithm. Also, the development of an efficient algorithm is tied to one's ability to understand pictorially and linguistically what the problem is asking. As students work toward trying to develop and use algorithms they may continue to draw pictures to help them think through the problem. However, they also need to learn to talk about what the problem is asking, what the answer means, what makes sense as a solution strategy, and how this language is related to the algorithm.

Our goal is to help students develop an efficient algorithm. Not all students may get to the "reciprocal" algorithm for division of fractions, but they should have efficient strategies that make sense to them to solve problems that call for division with fractions.

Understanding Division as an Operation

There are two situations associated with division. We can focus on division as a *sharing* operation in problems like this:

> Ms. Li brings peanuts to be shared equally by members of groups winning each game. How much of a pound of peanuts will each student get when the peanuts weigh $\frac{1}{2}$ pound and four students are on the winning team?

Here the question is how much each of the four team members will get if the amount is shared equally. You can also think of this as a *partitioning*, sometimes called *partitive*, model.

Another kind of situation calling for division is a *grouping* situation. For example:

> Naylah plans to make small cheese pizzas to sell at a school fundraiser. She has nine bars of cheese. How many pizzas can she make if each takes $\frac{1}{3}$ bar of cheese?

Here the question is how many groups of size $\frac{1}{3}$ can be made from nine bars of cheese? Another way to ask this is "How many $\frac{1}{3}$'s are in 9?" This kind of problem has multiple names—*measurement*, *subtractive*, or *quotitive* model. Knowing these names is not important for your students, but it is important for them to experience situations representing these different interpretations of division. Otherwise students will not have all the tools for deciding *when* division is the appropriate operation.

Developing a Division Algorithm

We develop understanding of division of fractions by looking at three cases—division of a whole number by a fraction, division of a fraction by a whole number, and division of a fraction by a fraction. From these situations, several approaches to division are developed: multiplying by the denominator and dividing by the numerator, multiplying by the reciprocal, and the common denominator approach.

Multiplying by the Denominator and Dividing by the Numerator When you confront a whole number divided by a fraction, such as $9 \div \frac{1}{3}$, it is easiest to interpret this as finding how many $\frac{1}{3}$'s are in 9. To answer, students find how many $\frac{1}{3}$'s are in a whole and multiply by 9 to find the total number of $\frac{1}{3}$'s in 9. The reasoning is as follows: In $9 \div \frac{1}{3}$, I have to find the total number of $\frac{1}{3}$'s in 9. I know that there are three $\frac{1}{3}$'s in 1, so there are 9×3 or 27 of the $\frac{1}{3}$'s in 9. In summary, $9 \div \frac{1}{3} = 9 \times 3 = 27$.

Next we move to $9 \div \frac{2}{3}$. A key to understanding in the development of division of fractions is the relationship between the two problems $9 \div \frac{1}{3}$ and $9 \div \frac{2}{3}$. The question is, how are the answers related and why? The answer to the first problem is 27 and the answer to the second is $13\frac{1}{2}$. Why does it make sense for the answer to the second to be half that of the first? You can interpret the first problem as how many $\frac{1}{3}$'s are in 9 and the second as how many $\frac{2}{3}$'s are in 9. Now it makes sense that it will take twice as much to make $\frac{2}{3}$ than to make $\frac{1}{3}$ so the number you can make will be half as large.

This conversation allows students to begin to relate a whole string of division problems, such as $9 \div \frac{1}{3}, 9 \div \frac{2}{3}, 9 \div \frac{3}{3}$, and $9 \div \frac{4}{3}$. Here we are building a case for thinking of division of fractions as multiplying by the denominator of the divisor to find how many in one whole and then dividing by the numerator because that is how many it takes to make a piece of the required size. These two actions are the same as multiplying by the reciprocal.

When moving to other cases, such as dividing a fraction by a whole number and dividing a fraction by a fraction, support student thinking with models. In these situations, we continue to see that multiplying by the denominator and dividing by the numerator makes sense because we can interpret what each part is accomplishing. In the computation $\frac{2}{3} \div \frac{3}{4}$, we can find the "answer" by multiplying by $\frac{4}{3}$. But what does this mean? Multiplying by 4 tells us how many $\frac{1}{4}$'s are in a whole and dividing by 3 adjusts this answer by accounting for the fact that it takes 3 of the $\frac{1}{4}$'s to make one object of the size the problem requires. We have found that many students are able to see the pattern of "multiply by the denominator and divide by the numerator of the divisor" and explain why it makes sense through this kind of classroom talk.

Multiplying by the Reciprocal The reciprocal approach may arise when working with fraction divided by whole number contexts. For example, with the problem $\frac{1}{2} \div 4$, students often draw the following diagram.

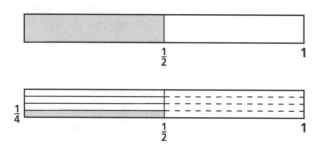

They may reason by saying, "I divided the $\frac{1}{2}$ into four parts so I could find $\frac{1}{4}$ of the half." Here students are relating the problem $\frac{1}{2} \div 4$ to the problem $\frac{1}{2} \times \frac{1}{4}$. This type of reasoning, the diagram that develops it, and the number sentences that support it, help students move from the division problem to multiplying by the reciprocal.

Common Denominator Approach Some students intuitively try the same approach for division that worked in addition and subtraction—finding a common denominator. This algorithm nicely links to their whole number understanding of division. For example, in the problem $\frac{7}{9} \div \frac{1}{3}$, students rename the fractions to say $\frac{7}{9} \div \frac{3}{9}$. The common denominator allows them to reason that if they have 7 one-ninth sized pieces of something and want to find out how many groups of 3 one-ninth sized pieces they can make, they can find the answer from the computation $7 \div 3$, which equals $2\frac{1}{3}$. This algorithm is used in *Bits and Pieces III* to develop decimal division.

Relating Multiplication and Division
In additive situations, those involving addition and subtraction, the quantities are easy to count, measure, combine and separate. This is because each quantity in an addition or subtraction problem has the same kind of label or is the same type of unit. For example, $3 + 4 = 7$ can be thought of as 3 marbles plus 4 marbles equals 7 marbles. Each quantity is a number of marbles.

In multiplicative situations, those involving multiplication and division, the quantities are not so straightforward. Each number may represent a different kind of unit. For example, if tomatoes cost $0.87 per can, the total cost for 6 cans can be found by multiplying 6 cans × 87 cents. It is hard to imagine a situation where adding tomatoes and money would make sense.

Another challenge is the different kinds of situations that call for multiplication and for division. A multiplication problem may be counting an array, or finding an area, or finding the sum of a repeated addition, and so on. Division may be finding how many groups of a certain size or measure that you can make from a given quantity or how many objects or parts would be in each of a given number of groups.

For example, the number sentence $3 \times 4 = 12$ could represent 3 people, each with 4 candies. The same number sentence could also represent 3 candies given to each of 4 people. The two types of division situations, sharing and grouping, are related to these two multiplication situations. The diagram in Figure 2 shows the grouping model of division first followed by the sharing model.

It is important that students develop a sense of the kinds of situations for which each operation is useful. Therefore, you will see attention to meanings and interpretation of the operation in the unit.

Inverse Relationships

Fact families and missing-value problems are used to introduce the inverse relationships of addition and subtraction, and multiplication and division. In elementary grades, students learn about *fact families* for whole numbers. For example, they learn that the addition problems $3 + 5$ and $5 + 3$ both equal 8. In addition, they are related to two subtraction sentences, $8 - 5 = 3$ and $8 - 3 = 5$. In this unit these ideas are expanded to include fractions. For example, students learn that the addition sentence $\frac{7}{10} + \frac{1}{2} = \frac{6}{5}$ is related to $\frac{1}{2} + \frac{7}{10} = \frac{6}{5}$ and two subtraction sentences, $\frac{6}{5} - \frac{1}{2} = \frac{7}{10}$ and $\frac{6}{5} - \frac{7}{10} = \frac{1}{2}$.

Understanding the inverse relationship between the operations pairs of addition-subtraction and multiplication-division is a tool that lends itself to many situations, one of which is equation solving. In this unit, missing-value problems are used to introduce students to the use of a variable as a placeholder. However, the focus is on understanding inverse relationships. We do not expect students to develop formal procedures or notation for solving algebraic equations at this stage.

Missing-value problems, as used in this unit, will help students begin to develop a generalized understanding of inverse relationships. This generalization is aided by working on these relationships in non-whole number contexts. In whole number contexts, such as $20 \div N = 5$, solving for N is partly aided by students using multiplication and division facts with which they had repeated experience. In a problem like $\frac{8}{15} \div N = \frac{2}{3}$, this becomes more difficult. Students have to think about which values are the factors in the related multiplication problems $\frac{2}{3} \times N = \frac{8}{15}$ and $N \times \frac{2}{3} = \frac{8}{15}$. Here, N and $\frac{2}{3}$ are the factors and $\frac{8}{15}$ is the product of the related multiplication problem. Going a step further, if you divide the term that represents the product of the multiplication problem by one of the factors you will get the other factor. This leads to the related missing-value problem $\frac{8}{15} \div \frac{2}{3} = N$ or the realization that if you divide $\frac{8}{15}$ by the known value $\frac{2}{3}$, you will get the other factor, N.

Keep in mind that inverse relationships will be explored in later units with other number contexts such as decimals and integers. For most students this will be an initial introduction and mastery is not expected. But over time, students will start to think beyond the actual numbers to the relationships that exist among the values in related addition and subtraction problems and multiplication and division problems, or fact families. This understanding will be a powerful tool for students to use in other mathematical contexts.

Figure 2

Grouping

3	×	4	=	12	→	12	÷	4	=	3
Unit		*Rate*		*Total*		*Total*		*Rate*		*Unit*
Number of people		Candy per person		Candies		Candies		Candy per person		Number of people

Sharing

3	×	4	=	12	→	12	÷	4	=	3
Rate		*Unit*		*Total*		*Total*		*Rate*		*Unit*
Candy per person		Number of people		Candies		Candies		Number of people		Candy per person

Content Connections to Other Units

Big Idea	Prior Work	Future Work
Performing mathematical operations with fractions	Interpreting fractions as part-whole relationships; combining and comparing fractions, partitioning and repartitioning fractions, finding equivalent fractions (*Bits and Pieces I*); factorization of numerators or denominators (*Prime Time*)	Interpreting fractions as probabilities (*How Likely Is It?*); interpreting fractions as scale factors, ratios, and proportions (*Stretching and Shrinking*); interpreting fractions as constants and variables in linear and nonlinear equations and relationships (*Variables and Patterns; Moving Straight Ahead; Thinking With Mathematical Models; Growing, Growing, Growing; Frogs, Fleas, and Painted Cubes; Say It With Symbols*); using fractions to help understand irrational numbers (*Looking for Pythagoras*); using fractions to understand integers (*Accentuate the Negative*); interpreting and applying fractions (*Bits and Pieces III; What Do You Expect?; Samples and Populations*)
Developing and applying algorithms for performing fraction calculations	Estimating to check reasonableness of answers (*Bits and Pieces I*)	Developing algorithms for finding the area and perimeter of 2-D shapes (*Covering and Surrounding*); developing algorithms for finding the volume and surface area of 3-D shapes (*Filling and Wrapping*); developing algorithms for integer computation (*Accentuate the Negative*); developing algorithms for decimal computation (*Bits and Pieces III*); applying fractions in studying probability (*How Likely Is It?; What Do You Expect?; Samples and Populations*); applying ratios, proportions, and scale factors (*Stretching and Shrinking; Comparing and Scaling*)
Inverse relationships and operations in fraction settings	Inverse operations in whole number settings (elementary school)	Inverse operations in decimal settings (*Bits and Pieces III*); inverse operations in integer settings (*Accentuate the Negative*); finding an unknown dimension given area or volume (*Covering and Surrounding; Filling and Wrapping*); solving algebraic equations (*Moving Straight Ahead; Thinking With Mathematical Models; Say it With Symbols*); patterns of change (*Moving Straight Ahead; Thinking With Mathematical Models*)
Performing mathematical operations with fractions	Interpreting fractions as part-whole relationships; combining and comparing fractions, partitioning and repartitioning fractions, finding equivalent fractions (*Bits and Pieces I*)	Interpreting fractions as probabilities (*How Likely Is It?*); interpreting fractions as scale factors, ratios, and proportions (*Stretching and Shrinking*); interpreting fractions as constants and variable coefficients in linear and nonlinear equations and relationships (*Variables and Patterns; Moving Straight Ahead; Thinking With Mathematical Models; Growing, Growing, Growing; Frogs, Fleas, and Painted Cubes; Say It With Symbols*); using fractions to help understand irrational numbers (*Looking for Pythagoras*); using fractions to understand integers (*Accentuate the Negative*); interpreting and applying fractions (*Bits and Pieces III; What Do You Expect?; Samples and Populations*)

Planning for the Unit

Pacing Suggestions and Materials

Investigations and Assessments	Pacing 45–50 min. classes	Materials for Students	Materials for Teachers
1 Estimating With Fractions	2 days	Labsheets 1.1A–1.1C, scissors	Transparency 1.1
Mathematical Reflections	$\frac{1}{2}$ day		
2 Adding and Subtracting Fractions	5 days	Labsheets 2.1, 2.2. 2ACE Exercise 1; large sheets of chart paper and markers (optional, instead of transparencies)	Transparencies 2.1, 2.2, 2.4A, 2.4B
Mathematical Reflections	$\frac{1}{2}$ day		
Assessment: Check Up	$\frac{1}{2}$ day		
3 Multiplying With Fractions	5 days	Labsheet 3.1, two different colored pencils, large sheets of chart paper and markers (optional, instead of transparencies)	Transparencies 3.2, 3.3, 3.4, 3.5
Mathematical Reflections	$\frac{1}{2}$ day		
Assessment: Partner Quiz	1 day		
4 Dividing With Fractions	5 days	Large sheets of chart paper (optional, instead of transparencies)	Transparencies 4.1, 4.4
Mathematical Reflections	$\frac{1}{2}$ day		
Looking Back and Looking Ahead	$\frac{1}{2}$ day		
Assessment: Self Assessment	Take Home		
Assessment: Unit Test	1 day		

Total Time 22 days	**Materials for Use in All Investigations**	
For detailed pacing for Problems within each Investigation, see the Suggested Pacing at the beginning of each Investigation.

For pacing with block scheduling, see next page. | Calculators, blank transparencies and transparency markers (optional), student notebooks | Blank transparencies and transparency markers (optional) |

Pacing for Block Scheduling (90-minute class periods)

Investigation	Suggested Pacing	Investigation	Suggested Pacing
Investigation 1	**$1\frac{1}{2}$ days**	**Investigation 3**	**3 days**
Problem 1.1	$\frac{1}{2}$ day	Problem 3.1	$\frac{1}{2}$ day
Problem 1.2	$\frac{1}{2}$ day	Problem 3.2	$\frac{1}{2}$ day
Math Reflections	$\frac{1}{2}$ day	Problem 3.3	$\frac{1}{2}$ day
Investigation 2	**$3\frac{1}{2}$ days**	Problem 3.4	$\frac{1}{2}$ day
Problem 2.1	1 day	Problem 3.5	$\frac{1}{2}$ day
Problem 2.2	$\frac{1}{2}$ day	Math Reflections	$\frac{1}{2}$ day
Problem 2.3	$\frac{1}{2}$ day	**Investigation 4**	**$3\frac{1}{2}$ days**
Problem 2.4	1 day	Problem 4.1	1 day
Math Reflections	$\frac{1}{2}$ day	Problem 4.2	$\frac{1}{2}$ day
		Problem 4.3	$\frac{1}{2}$ day
		Problem 4.4	1 day
		Math Reflections	$\frac{1}{2}$ day

Vocabulary

Essential Terms Developed in This Unit	Useful Terms Referenced in This Unit	Terms Developed in Previous Units
algorithm fact family	mathematical sentence overestimate reciprocal underestimate	benchmark decimal fraction percent unit fraction denominator equivalent fraction improper fraction mixed number numerator number sentence factor multiple least common multiple

Go Online
PHSchool.com

For: Multiple-Choice Skills Practice
Web Code: amk-5500

Components

Use the chart below to quickly see which components are available for each Investigation.

Investigation	Labsheets	Additional Practice	Transparencies		Formal Assessment		Assessment Options	
			Problem	Summary	Check Up	Partner Quiz	Multiple-Choice	Question Bank
1	1.1A–C	✔	1.1				✔	✔
2	2.1, 2.2, 2ACE Exercise 1	✔	2.1, 2.2, 2.4A, 2.4B		✔		✔	✔
3	3.1	✔	3.2, 3.3, 3.4, 3.5			✔	✔	✔
4		✔	4.1, 4.4				✔	
For the Unit		*ExamView* CD-ROM, Web site			Unit Test, Notebook Check, Self Assessment		Multiple-Choice, Question Bank, *ExamView* CD-ROM	

Also Available For Use With This Unit

- Parent Guide: take-home letter for the unit
- Implementing CMP

- Spanish Assessment Resources
- Additional online and technology resources

Technology

The Use of Calculators

Connected Mathematics was developed with the belief that calculators should be available and that students should learn when their use is appropriate. For this reason, we do not designate specific problems as "calculator problems." However, in this unit, we suggest that students refrain from using calculators so that they are able to understand and able to operate with fractions. Rushing to use the calculator does not promote a deep analysis of why fraction operations work, how to compute an answer, and what an answer means.

Student Activity CD-ROM

Includes interactive activities to enhance the learning in the Problems within Investigations.

PHSchool.com

For Students Multiple-choice practice with instant feedback, updated data sources, data sets for Tinkerplots data software.

For Teachers Professional development, curriculum support, downloadable forms, and more.

See also www.math.msu.edu/cmp for more resources for both teachers and students.

ExamView® CD-ROM

Create multiple versions of practice sheets and tests for course objectives and standardized tests. Includes dynamic questions, online testing, student reports, and all test and practice items in Spanish. Also includes all items in the Assessment Resources and Additional Practice.

Teacher Express™ CD-ROM

Includes a lesson planning tool, the Teacher's Guide pages, and all the teaching resources.

LessonLab Online Courses

LessonLab offers comprehensive, facilitated professional development designed to help teachers implement CMP and improve student achievement. To learn more, please visit PHSchool.com/cmp2.

Assessment Summary

Ongoing Informal Assessment

Embedded in the Student Unit

Problems Use students' work from the Problems to informally check student understanding.

ACE exercises Use ACE exercises for homework assignments to assess student understanding.

Mathematical Reflections Have students summarize their learning at the end of each Investigation.

Looking Back and Looking Ahead At the end of the unit, use the first two sections to allow students to show what they know about the unit.

Additional Resources

Teacher's Guide Use the Check for Understanding feature of some Summaries and the probing questions that appear in the *Launch, Explore,* or *Summarize* sections of all Investigations to check student understanding.

Summary Transparencies Use these transparencies to focus class attention on a summary check for understanding.

Self Assessment

Notebook Check Students use this tool to organize and check their notebooks before giving them to their teacher. Located in *Assessment Resources*.

Self Assessment At the end of the unit, students reflect on and provide examples of what they learned. Located in *Assessment Resources*.

Formal Assessment

Choose the assessment materials that are appropriate for your students.

Assessment	For Use After	Focus	Student Work
Check Up	Invest. 2	Skills	Individual
Partner Quiz	Invest. 3	Rich problems	Pair
Unit Test	The Unit	Skills, rich problems	Individual

Additional Resources

Multiple-Choice Items Use these items for homework, review, a quiz, or add them to the Unit Test.

Question Bank Choose from these questions for homework, review, or replacements for Quiz, Check Up, or Unit Test questions.

Additional Practice Choose practice exercises for each investigation for homework, review, or formal assessments.

***ExamView* Test Generator** Create practice sheets, review quizzes, and tests with this dynamic software. Give online tests and receive student progress reports. (All test items are also available in Spanish.)

Spanish Assessment Resources

Includes Partner Quizzes, Check Ups, Unit Test, Multiple-Choice Items, Question Bank, Notebook Check, and Self Assessment. Plus, the *ExamView* Test Generator has all test items in Spanish.

Correlation to Standardized Tests

Investigation	NAEP	Terra Nova CAT6	Terra Nova CTBS	ITBS	SAT10	Local Test
1 Estimating With Fractions	N1e, N2a, N2b	✔	✔		✔	
2 Adding and Subtracting Fractions	N3a, N3f, N5e	✔	✔	✔	✔	
3 Multiplying With Fractions	N1b, N3a, N5e	✔	✔	✔	✔	
4 Dividing With Fractions	N1b, N3a, N5e		✔	✔		

NAEP National Assessment of Educational Progress

CAT6/Terra Nova California Achievement Test, 6th Ed.
CTBS/Terra Nova Comprehensive Test of Basic Skills

ITBS Iowa Test of Basic Skills, Form M
SAT10 Stanford Achievement Test, 10th Ed.

Using the Unit Opener

Discuss the questions posed on the opening page of the Student Edition, which are designed to start students thinking about the kinds of questions and mathematics in the unit. They also give you an informal assessment of what students already know about fractions and fraction operations. Don't expect all students to be able to answer "correctly" at this time. Do, however, present an opportunity for the class to discuss the questions and to start to think about what is needed to answer them. You may want to revisit these questions as students learn the mathematical ideas and techniques necessary to find the answers.

Problems in contexts are used to help students informally reason about the mathematics of the unit. The problems are deliberately sequenced to develop understanding of concepts and skills. Contexts, models, estimation, and writing number sentences help students develop skills, strategies, and algorithms for fraction operations.

Using the Mathematical Highlights

The Mathematical Highlights page in the Student Edition provides information to students, parents, and other family members. It gives students a preview of the mathematics and some of the overarching questions that they should ask themselves while studying *Bits and Pieces II*.

As they work through the unit, students can refer back to the Mathematical Highlights page to review what they have learned and to preview what is still to come. This page also tells students' families what mathematical ideas and activities will be covered as the class works through *Bits and Pieces II*.

Connected  Mathematics 2™

Bits and Pieces II

Using Fraction Operations

Glenda Lappan

James T. Fey

William M. Fitzgerald

Susan N. Friel

Elizabeth Difanis Phillips

PEARSON

Boston, Massachusetts · Glenview, Illinois · Shoreview, Minnesota · Upper Saddle River, New Jersey

Notes _____

_____

_____

_____

Bits and Pieces II

Understanding Fraction Operations

Last season Farmer Sam picked $1\frac{3}{4}$ bushels of tomatoes from his kitchen garden and $14\frac{1}{3}$ bushels from his canning garden. About how many total bushels of tomatoes did he harvest?

Blaine plans to paint a highway stripe that is $\frac{9}{10}$ of a mile long. He is $\frac{2}{3}$ of the way done when he runs out of paint. How long is the stripe he painted?

There are 12 baby rabbits at the pet store. Gabriella has $5\frac{1}{4}$ ounces of parsley to feed the rabbits as treats. She wants to give each rabbit the same amount. How much parsley does each rabbit get?

Notes _____

_____

_____

_____

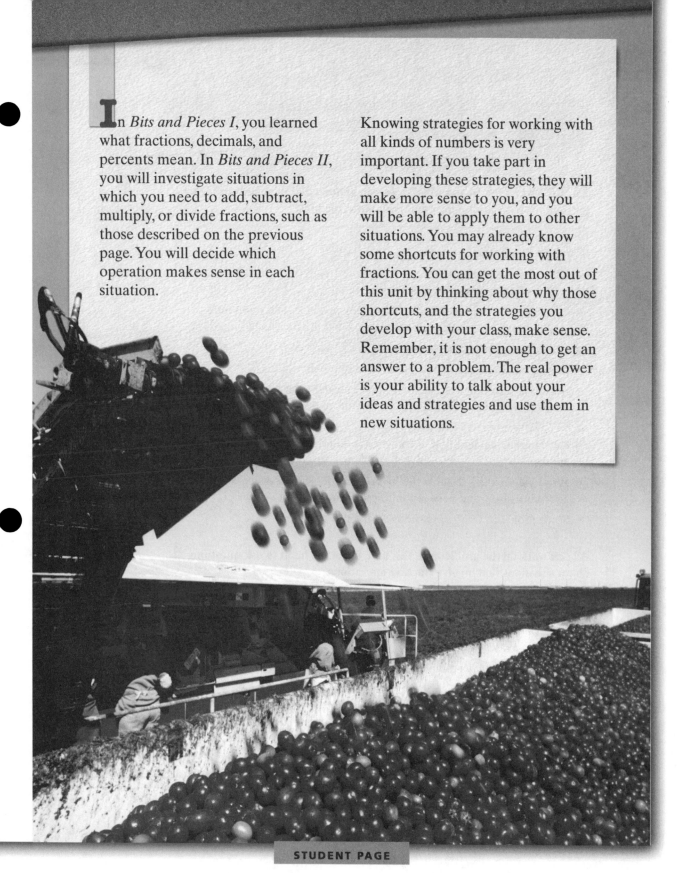

In *Bits and Pieces I*, you learned what fractions, decimals, and percents mean. In *Bits and Pieces II*, you will investigate situations in which you need to add, subtract, multiply, or divide fractions, such as those described on the previous page. You will decide which operation makes sense in each situation.

Knowing strategies for working with all kinds of numbers is very important. If you take part in developing these strategies, they will make more sense to you, and you will be able to apply them to other situations. You may already know some shortcuts for working with fractions. You can get the most out of this unit by thinking about why those shortcuts, and the strategies you develop with your class, make sense. Remember, it is not enough to get an answer to a problem. The real power is your ability to talk about your ideas and strategies and use them in new situations.

Notes

Mathematical Highlights

Understanding Fraction Operations

In *Bits and Pieces II*, you will develop an understanding of and strategies for the four basic arithmetic operations with fractions.

You will learn how to

- Use benchmarks and other strategies to estimate the reasonableness of results of operations with fractions
- Develop ways to model sums, differences, products, and quotients, including the use of areas, fraction strips, and number lines
- Use estimates and exact solutions to make decisions
- Look for rules to generalize patterns in numbers
- Use your knowledge of fractions and equivalence of fractions to develop algorithms for adding, subtracting, multiplying and dividing fractions
- Recognize when addition, subtraction, multiplication, or division is the appropriate operation to solve a problem
- Write fact families to show the inverse relationship between addition and subtraction, and between multiplication and division
- Solve problems using operations on fractions

As you work on the problems in this unit, make it a habit to ask questions about situations that involve fraction operations.

What models or diagrams might be helpful in understanding the situation and the relationships among quantities?

What models or diagrams might help decide which operation is useful in solving a problem?

What is a reasonable estimate for the answer?

Notes _____

_____

_____

_____

 **Estimating With Fractions**

Mathematical and Problem-Solving Goals

- Use benchmarks and decimal-fraction relationships to develop estimation strategies for finding fraction and decimal sums

- Use estimation skills in contextual situations where an exact answer is not needed to make an informed decision

- Make decisions about whether an overestimate or an underestimate will suffice

Summary of Problems

Problem 1.1 Getting Close

Students estimate sums of fractions and decimals to determine if each sum is nearest 0, 1, 2, or 3.

Problem 1.2 Estimating Sums

Students learn estimation strategies in contextual situations and consider whether they need an overestimate or an underestimate.

Mathematics Background

For background on estimation, see page 5.

	Suggested Pacing	Materials for Students	Materials for Teachers	ACE Assignments
All	$2\frac{1}{2}$ days	Calculators; colored pens, pencils, or markers; blank transparencies and transparency markers (optional); student notebooks	Blank transparencies and transparency markers	
1.1	1 day	Labsheets 1.1A and 1.1B (1 set per group), Labsheet 1.1C (1 set of 0, 1, 2, and 3 per student; optional: 1 set of $\frac{1}{2}$, $1\frac{1}{2}$, and $2\frac{1}{2}$ per student), scissors	Transparency 1.1	1–25, 31–35, 43–47
1.2	1 day			26–30, 36–42
MR	$\frac{1}{2}$ day			

Goal

- Use benchmarks and decimal-fraction relationships to develop estimation strategies for finding fraction and decimal sums

In this section, students play a game based on estimating sums of fractions and decimals. Decimal and fraction cards are mixed to help students build flexibility in moving between representations. While playing the game, students practice making estimates and explore estimation strategies.

The last part of the summary introduces the terms *underestimate* and *overestimate*. Problem 1.2 asks students to decide if a situation calls for an underestimate or an overestimate. You might find it helpful to read the introduction to Problem 1.2 in the Teacher's Guide so that you can see how Problem 1.2 builds off of Problem 1.1.

Launch 1.1

Use the introduction to review whole-number benchmarks and selecting the nearest benchmark for a number. Students did a similar activity in *Bits and Pieces I*. Talk about $\frac{3}{8}$ and 0.58. You might want to provide a few more examples.

Suggested Questions Draw a number line marked with 0, 1, and 2 on the board, provide students with a fraction or decimal, and ask questions like the following:

- *About where does $\frac{4}{9}$ belong on the number line and why?* (Between 0 and 1, but close to $\frac{1}{2}$ because half of 9 is 4.5, or $4\frac{1}{2}$, so 4 out of 9 is close to $\frac{1}{2}$.)

- *Is $\frac{4}{9}$ closer to 0 or 1? Why?* (Since $\frac{4}{9}$ is a little less than $\frac{1}{2}$ it is closer to 0.)

- *How far is it from 0?* ($\frac{4}{9}$)

- *How far is it from 1?* ($\frac{5}{9}$)

When students are comfortable with estimating the placement of a single number, look at the Getting Ready. Here students are asked to estimate the sum of two numbers and decide whether the sum is closest to 0, 1, or 2.

- *Is the sum of $\frac{1}{2} + \frac{5}{8}$ between 0 and 1 or between 1 and 2?* (Since one number is exactly $\frac{1}{2}$ and the other number is more than $\frac{1}{2}$ the sum will be between 1 and 2.)

- *Is the sum closer to 1 or closer to 2?* (Closer to 1 because $\frac{5}{8}$, which is just an eighth more than $\frac{1}{2}$, added to exactly $\frac{1}{2}$, is just an eighth more than 1.)

In addition to the examples in the Getting Ready, the following problems could also be used. These examples use benchmarks from 0 to 3—like the game situation in Getting Close.

Classroom Dialogue Model

Teacher Which benchmark, 0, 1, 2, or 3, is the actual sum $\frac{3}{8} + \frac{5}{7}$ nearest?

Emily I think it is closest to 1 because $\frac{5}{7} = \frac{4}{7} + \frac{1}{7}$ and $\frac{4}{7}$ is a little over $\frac{1}{2}$. Three eighths is a little under $\frac{1}{2}$. So $\frac{3}{8} + \frac{4}{7}$ is about 1 and the extra $\frac{1}{7}$ is not enough to get near 2.

Teacher Here is another sum to estimate. Which benchmark, 0, 1, 2, or 3, is the sum $\frac{2}{3} + 1\frac{2}{5}$ nearest?

Carlos It cannot be 1 because of the $1\frac{2}{5}$. That much is already over 1.

Paul I think it is nearer 2 because if $1\frac{2}{5}$ were $1\frac{2.5}{5}$, that would be $1\frac{1}{2}$. So the sum must be nearer to 2.

Sula The sum has to be near 2 since $\frac{2}{3}$ is more than $\frac{1}{2}$ and $1\frac{2}{5}$ is close to $1\frac{1}{2}$.

Teacher Is the actual sum greater than or less than the estimated sum of 2?

Andrea Since $\frac{2}{6}$ is less than $\frac{2}{5}$ and $\frac{2}{6} = \frac{1}{3}$, $\frac{2}{3} + \frac{2}{5}$ is greater than 1. The actual sum has to be a little over 2.

Alex $1\frac{2}{3}$ is $\frac{1}{3}$ less than 2 but we have a bit more to add. So I thought about whether $\frac{2}{5}$ was enough to make the actual sum go over 2. Since $\frac{2}{5}$ is more than $\frac{2}{6}$, or $\frac{1}{3}$, the actual sum goes over 2!

Brian I used decimals. $1\frac{2}{5} = 1\frac{4}{10}$, which is 1.4. If I add 0.6 to 1.4, I will get exactly 2. But $\frac{2}{3}$ is 0.66, which is greater than 0.6, so the actual sum is a little over 2.

Teacher Suppose the sum you are going to estimate has fractions and decimals, such as the following: $\frac{3}{4} + 0.38$.

Richard Oh, then you need to think about the decimal as a fraction. Since 0.38 is about $\frac{2}{5}$, and $\frac{2}{5}$ is greater than $\frac{1}{4}$, I would say that the sum is a little over 1.

Sarah But can't you estimate the fraction as a decimal? I would say $\frac{3}{4}$ is 0.75 and then get about 1.15, which is near 1.

You might want to tell your class that they can write sentences to show their estimated sums, but they should not use an equal sign since the answer is an estimate. Introduce the *approximately equal to* sign, $\approx$.

When you are comfortable that the class is thinking about strategies for using benchmarks to estimate sums, explain that they are going to play a game that involves fractions, decimals, and the use of estimation, addition, and benchmarks.

Read through the rules for playing the Getting Close game, and make sure students understand how to play. You might have two students play a couple of rounds to demonstrate. Also look at the questions that students need to answer after they have played the game. Read Question A together and point out that it asks them to reflect upon the game.

Distribute a set of four number squares (0, 1, 2, and 3) to each student and a set of Getting Close cards to each group. This game works well for two to four people.

Explore 1.1

Have your students play a few games. Tell them to share their strategies after each round. As you listen to groups share their strategies, make a note of interesting strategies to share in the summary.

After students have played at least one full game, remind them about Question A in Problem 1.1.

- *When you play the game this time, think about the two questions in part (2) of Question A.*

At some point, have students stop playing the game and answer the questions.

Challenge

For students who are not challenged enough using 0, 1, 2, and 3 as benchmarks, suggest they play a different version of the game called Getting Even Closer. It uses the same rules, but students add the benchmarks $\frac{1}{2}$, $1\frac{1}{2}$, and $2\frac{1}{2}$ to their number squares. This version of the game can also be used as a follow-up activity.

Summarize 1.1

Question A

Suggested Questions Before discussing the strategies students found for estimating sums, you might want to ask questions about other elements of the game, such as:

- *What kinds of sums were easy to estimate?*

Have students share their thinking about why some game pieces were easy to estimate.

- *Were there times that you found the actual sum because it was just as quick as estimating?* (Students might offer a few examples like $\frac{2}{5} + \frac{1}{5}$ where the actual sum is $\frac{3}{5}$.)
- *Did you find it easier if the cards were either both decimals or both fractions?*
- *Were there any sums that were difficult to estimate? What made them difficult?*
- *What did you do when one card was a fraction and the other was a decimal?*

Look at several situations from the game cards. Begin by asking students to discuss a reasonable estimate for the sum and their strategies for finding it. For example,

- *If you and your partner turned over the game cards $\frac{4}{9}$ and $1\frac{1}{3}$, how would you decide what whole number, or benchmark, the sum is nearest?* (The sum is closest to 2 because $\frac{4}{9}$ is about $\frac{1}{2}$ and $1\frac{1}{3}$ is about $1\frac{1}{2}$, so $\frac{1}{2} + 1\frac{1}{2}$ is 2.)

- *Is 2 a reasonable estimate?* (yes)

- *Did someone think about the problem a different way?*

After students describe their strategies for a few problems, shift the conversation to introducing overestimate and underestimate, the focus of Problem 1.2.

- *With $\frac{4}{9}$ and $1\frac{1}{3}$, is the actual sum exactly 2, less than 2, or greater than 2?* (Less than 2. $\frac{4}{9}$ is a little less than $\frac{1}{2}$ and $1\frac{1}{3}$ is a little less than $1\frac{1}{2}$. Since the estimates are greater than the actual numbers, the sum of the estimates is greater than the actual sum. This means that the actual sum is less than 2.)

- *Suppose two fractions, each less than $\frac{1}{2}$, are added. What can you tell me about the actual sum?* (Since $\frac{1}{2} + \frac{1}{2} = 1$, a number less than $\frac{1}{2}$ plus another number less than $\frac{1}{2}$ must be less than 1.)

- *If you use $\frac{1}{2} + \frac{1}{2} = 1$ as the estimated sum, but the actual fractions are less than $\frac{1}{2}$, is your estimated sum an overestimate or an underestimate of the actual sum? Why?* (The estimate is more than the actual sum, so it is an overestimate.)

- *Suppose two fractions, each a little greater than $1\frac{1}{2}$, are added. What can you tell me about the actual sum? Why?* (Since the actual values are greater than $1\frac{1}{2}$, the actual sum is greater than 3.)

- *If you use $1\frac{1}{2} + 1\frac{1}{2} = 3$ for the estimated sum, but the actual fractions are both a little greater than $1\frac{1}{2}$, is your estimated sum an overestimate or an underestimate? Why?* (The estimated sum is less than the actual sum so the estimated sum is an underestimate.)

When posing these questions verbally, they can be confusing. It is helpful to write out an actual problem with the estimate below. For example:

Actual sum $\frac{2}{3} + \frac{5}{9} = \blacksquare$

Estimated sum $\frac{1}{2} + \frac{1}{2} = 1$

- *Is the estimated sum greater than or less than the actual sum?* (less than)

- *How do you know?* (Both $\frac{2}{3}$ and $\frac{5}{9}$ are greater than $\frac{1}{2}$, so the actual sum is greater than 1.)

- *Is your estimated sum an underestimate or an overestimate of the actual sum?* (The estimated sum of 1 is less than the actual sum. So the estimated sum is an underestimate of the actual answer.)

Question B
Suggested Questions

- *Given the game cards $\frac{3}{10}, \frac{1}{5}, \frac{3}{4}, 0.25,$ and $0.33,$ what are the greatest and least sums possible?* (Least is $\frac{1}{5} + 0.25$, greatest is $\frac{3}{4} + 0.33$.)

- *What are some strategies you found useful in the game?*

Conclude the discussion by asking students to share their strategies for estimating sums of fractions and decimals. It helps to show their answers as number sentences (also called mathematical sentences) with an *approximately equal to* sign, $\approx$. Some strategies students have used are shown below.

- Round the numbers being added to get "nice" numbers that can be manipulated mentally. For example, to estimate $\frac{9}{10} + 0.875$, round both numbers to 1 and estimate the sum as 2. To estimate $0.67 + \frac{4}{7}$, round both numbers to $\frac{1}{2}$ and estimate the sum as 1.

- If the numbers are in different forms, rename one of them so they are both fractions or both decimals. For example, to compute $\frac{1}{4} + 1.1$, convert $\frac{1}{4}$ to 0.25 and add the two decimals.

- Use benchmarks. For example, $\frac{1}{10}$ is close to 0, and 1.125 is close to 1, so $\frac{1}{10} + 1.125$ is close to $0 + 1$, or 1.

Mathematical Goal

- Use benchmarks and decimal-fraction relationships to develop estimation strategies for finding fraction and decimal sums

Launch

Use the introduction to Problem 1.1 and the Getting Ready to review benchmarks and introduce estimating sums.

- *Is the sum of $\frac{1}{2} + \frac{5}{8}$ between 0 and 1 or between 1 and 2?*
- *Is the sum closer to 1 or closer to 2?*

Work through a few more examples where students have to estimate the sum of two numbers and explain their reasoning.

Introduce the *approximately equal to* sign, $\approx$, to use in estimation number sentences. Students should not use an equal sign since the answer is an estimate.

Read through the rules for playing the Getting Close game.

Distribute a set of number squares (0, 1, 2, and 3) to each student and a set of Getting Close cards to each group.

This game works best for two to four people.

Materials

- Transparency 1.1
- Labsheets 1.1A–1.1C
- scissors

Vocabulary

- benchmarks (review)

Explore

Have your students play a few games. After at least one full game, remind students about Question A in Problem 1.1. Remind them to share their strategies after each round and, after a few rounds, to write out their strategies.

Challenge

Suggest students play Getting Even Closer. It uses the same rules, but students add $\frac{1}{2}$, $1\frac{1}{2}$, and $2\frac{1}{2}$ to their number squares.

Summarize

Consider asking:

- *What kind of sums were easy to estimate? Were there times that you found the actual sum because it was just as quick as estimating?*
- *Did you find it easier if the cards were either both decimals or both fractions?*
- *Were there any sums that were difficult to estimate? What made them difficult?*
- *What did you do when one card was a fraction and the other was a decimal?*

Materials

- Student notebooks

Vocabulary

- overestimate
- underestimate

continued on next page

Look at several situations from the game cards.

- *If you and your partner turned over the game cards $\frac{4}{9}$ and $1\frac{1}{3}$, how would you decide what whole number, or benchmark, the sum is nearest?*

- *Is the actual sum exactly 2, less than 2, or greater than 2?*

- *Suppose two fractions, each less than $\frac{1}{2}$ are added. What can you tell me about the actual sum? Why? If you use 1 as the estimated sum, is that an overestimate or an underestimate of the actual sum? How do you know?*

Conclude the discussion by asking students to share their strategies for estimating sums of fractions and decimals.

ACE Assignment Guide for Problem 1.1

Core 1–15, 19–22, 31–33, 35
Other *Applications* 16–18, 23–25;
Connections 34; *Extensions* 43–47

Adapted For suggestions about adapting ACE exercises, see the CMP *Special Needs Handbook*.
Connecting to Prior Units 31–35: *Bits and Pieces 1*

Answers to Problem 1.1

A. 1. Answers will vary. One possible strategy is to use benchmarks and another is to think of decimals as money.

2. Answers will vary. Possible explanations: It was easy when each of the two cards was greater than $1\frac{1}{2}$. You knew the sum was closest to 3. It was hard when one card was a fraction and one was a decimal.

B. Students may not be able to compute the greatest and least sums. However, they should be able to choose the addends that would result in the greatest and least sums.

1. $\frac{3}{4} + 0.33 > 1$

2. $\frac{1}{5} + 0.25 < \frac{1}{2}$

Goals

- Use estimation skills in contextual situations where an exact answer is not needed to make an informed decision

- Make decisions about whether an overestimate or an underestimate will suffice

Problem 1.2 asks students to evaluate a situation and decide if they need an underestimate or an overestimate. When playing the Getting Close game, students had to estimate to decide what number the exact sum was nearest. The context of the game did not require students to think about whether their estimate was over the exact answer or under the exact answer.

One thing to note when estimating in contextual situations is that a decision is made based on the information one has. For example, it would not be appropriate to say that you can adjust all the values down, or up, or to the nearest whole number. It all depends on what the problem is asking and what the values are. It is important that the context is considered, and what the actual values are, before deciding what to do. A good example of this is Question C, which is discussed in the summary.

There are two key questions that are useful when deciding whether an overestimate or an underestimate is needed in Problem 1.2.

- Is the estimated sum less than (an underestimate of) or greater than (an overestimate of) the actual sum?

- What does the estimated sum tell you about how much material you should actually buy? Or what does the estimated sum tell you about how much lace you actually have?

The language of *estimated sum* and *actual sum*, as opposed to estimate and sum, will help make the intent of questions clear and focus students on thinking about the overall effect of their estimation.

Launch 1.2

Explain to students that they are going to practice estimating in realistic situations. They will be given situations for which they have to decide whether they need an overestimate or an underestimate.

Suggested Questions Start with a few questions with numbers and no context to reintroduce the notion of underestimate and overestimate.

- *Suppose you want to estimate the sum $1\frac{5}{6} + 1\frac{7}{8}$. What is a good estimate for the actual sum?* (Four. $1\frac{5}{6} + 1\frac{7}{8}$ is close to $2 + 2$.)

- *Is the estimated sum greater than or less than the actual sum?* (The estimated sum is greater than the actual sum. This means the estimated sum is an overestimate of the actual sum. So $2 + 2 > 1\frac{5}{6} + 1\frac{7}{8}$.)

- *Someone suggests that a reasonable estimate for $1\frac{5}{6} + 1\frac{7}{8}$ can be found by adding $1\frac{1}{2} + 1\frac{1}{2}$. What is this estimated sum?* (three)

- *Is $1\frac{1}{2} + 1\frac{1}{2} = 3$ an overestimate of the actual sum or an underestimate?* (It is an underestimate because the estimated sum is less than the actual sum. $1\frac{1}{2} + 1\frac{1}{2} < 1\frac{5}{6} + 1\frac{7}{8}$.)

- *What do these two estimates tell you about the actual sum?* (It is somewhere between 3 and 4.)

- *Are both estimates reasonable?* (yes)

- *What about the estimate $1\frac{1}{2} + 2 = 3\frac{1}{2}$? Is it closer to or further from the actual sum?* (Since $1\frac{5}{6}$ was reduced and $1\frac{7}{8}$ was increased, it is probably closer to the actual answer.)

- *Is this an overestimate of the actual answer or an underestimate?* (It is hard to tell since it is close. It is probably an underestimate, though, since reducing $\frac{5}{6}$ to $\frac{1}{2}$ is a greater change than increasing $\frac{7}{8}$ to 1.)

- *What if you are buying fencing for a small garden and the actual lengths you need are $1\frac{5}{6}$ ft and $1\frac{7}{8}$ ft? Which of these three estimates is useful? Would you want to buy 3 ft, $3\frac{1}{2}$ ft, or 4 ft of fencing?* (You should overestimate with 4 ft, so you can be sure you have enough. Three feet is an underestimate, and it will not be enough. Using $3\frac{1}{2}$ feet is close, but with 4 you can be sure you have enough.)

- *When you are working with only numbers, any of these three estimates are reasonable. But in real-life situations, you often choose a specific type of estimate.*

- *Name some situations where you might want to overestimate.* (food for a party, getting supplies, money needed for shopping, gas for a trip)

- *Name some situations where you might want to underestimate.* (trimming off something like hair or fabric, amount of weight a chair or an elevator can hold, an older person's age)

Introduce Problem 1.2 to your students.

- *Questions A–C will help you think more about what an overestimate or an underestimate is and when you want to use each one.*

Read through Question A with the students to be sure they understand what they are expected to do. You may need to explain to them that molding is a strip of wood added to decorate a wall. It would be okay to summarize after Questions A–C are done and assign Question D for homework.

This is a good problem with which to use a Think-Pair-Share classroom organization. Start the problem by having students work individually and then have them pair up with another student to share their reasoning and finish the problem.

(**Explore 1.2**)

Some students may struggle with deciding if they are overestimating or underestimating. You might suggest that they first do their estimate and then decide if they overestimated or underestimated.

Suggested Questions As students work, they may need help focusing on the actual sum and the estimated sum. Ask questions that let you assess student reasoning.

- *Is your estimated sum greater than (an overestimate of) or less than (an underestimate of) your actual sum?*

- *When you rounded the addends to the nearest benchmarks, did you increase or decrease each number to get a benchmark?*

- *What does the estimated sum tell you about how much material or lace you should actually buy?*

Pay particular attention to how students reason about Question B. In parts (2) and (3) of Question B, it is not important to get at an efficient strategy or algorithm. The focus should stay on questions like the following:

- *What is a reasonable estimate for the amount of material Madison needs?* (a little more than one yard)

- *Based on your estimate, whose solution is reasonable?* (Jamar's solution is reasonable because the actual sum is greater than 1.)

Have students talk about their estimates for Question C. Students may struggle with part (3) where they are asked to find a common denominator for four fractions. You might need to help them connect this question to what Jamar did in Question B. It might also help to solve the Question in parts:

- *Look at the first two lengths of lace: $1\frac{1}{3}$ yd and $2\frac{5}{6}$ yd. If you have to rewrite one or both of those numbers to have the same denominator, what might you choose for the denominator?* (6 or 12)

- *Now can you find a way to rewrite each of the four fractions so they all have the same denominator?*

- *Of what number would 3, 6, 8, and 12 all be a factor?* (24)

Question D asks students to estimate without a context. Making an overestimate or an underestimate is not the focus. The focus is on making a reasonable estimate.

When the students have completed most of the questions and you judge that a conversation about them is timely, move to the Summary.

Suggested Questions Have students share their estimates for Question A and why they think it is an underestimate or an overestimate.

- *Without computing an exact answer, how can you tell whether Elaine has enough wood molding?* (If you use $2\frac{1}{4}$ instead of $2\frac{3}{8}$ the estimated sum is exactly $5\frac{1}{2}$. Since the estimated sum is less than the actual sum, it is an underestimate.)

- *How does this help you know if Elaine has enough molding?* (Using lesser values for the estimated sum shows that Elaine needs more molding than she has.)

It might help to write this for students to see:

Actual sum $3\frac{1}{4} + 2\frac{3}{8} = \blacksquare$

Estimated sum $3\frac{1}{4} + 2\frac{1}{4} = 5\frac{1}{2}$

Estimated sum $<$ Actual sum

$3\frac{1}{4} + 2\frac{1}{4} < 3\frac{1}{4} + 2\frac{3}{8}$

Some students may use an estimate that does not help them decide if Elaine has enough molding. For example, rounding to the nearest half would give a good estimate in a non-contextual situation, but it will not help them decide if Elaine has enough molding.

Actual sum $3\frac{1}{4} + 2\frac{3}{8} = \blacksquare$

Estimated sum $3\frac{1}{4} + 2\frac{1}{2} = 6$

Estimated sum $>$ Actual sum

$3\frac{1}{2} + 2\frac{1}{2} > 3\frac{1}{4} + 2\frac{3}{8}$

Suggested Questions Call on someone to describe how he or she solved part (1) of Question B.

- *Is this a situation where you need an underestimate or an overestimate? Why?* (You want to overestimate how much material to buy so you can be sure you have enough.)

- *What is a reasonable estimate that lets you be sure you have enough material to make the curtains?* (By using greater values, $\frac{3}{4} + \frac{3}{4}$ or $1 + 1$, you can be sure you have enough material to make the actual curtains.)

Parts (2) and (3) of Question B introduce what students will learn in the next investigation, an algorithm for finding an exact answer. The purpose is to only raise the issue of finding an exact answer and to highlight the role of using a common denominator when adding quantities.

- *What do you think about Madison's reasoning?* (If you estimate, you can tell that her strategy does not make sense. All of the values are a little bit more than $\frac{1}{2}$. $\frac{1}{2} + \frac{1}{2} = \frac{1}{2}$ is not reasonable.)

- *What do you think about Jamar's reasoning?* (Jamar's approach leads to a solution that is close to the estimated answer. His solution is reasonable.)

- *Why do you think Jamar's strategy gives a reasonable answer?* (He is renaming the fractions so they both use the same size parts. It is easy to add them and see how many twenty fourths there are total.)

Be sure it is clear to students that Madison's strategy does not make sense so that they do not mistake adding numerators and adding denominators as a reasonable strategy. As students share their ideas about what Jamar is thinking, do not push for closure. Make it clear that renaming fractions to have the same denominators is a sensible strategy, but leave the conversation open so students can decide for themselves if this strategy makes sense all the time. The students will have additional opportunities to consider Jamar's strategy and to articulate an efficient algorithm for adding in Investigation 2.

When discussing Question C, look for strategies students are using to estimate sums or differences with fractions. When deciding if the estimate is an overestimate or an underestimate, focus students' thinking on how the estimated sum compares to the actual sum.

In this problem, Elaine needs 5 yards of lace. We are trying to figure out if the lengths she has will be at least 5 yards long.

- *Will Elaine have enough lace? How do you know?*

One approach students might use is to show that you can get a total of 5 without using all the values.

Actual sum $1\frac{1}{3} + 2\frac{5}{6} + \frac{7}{8} + \frac{5}{12} = \blacksquare$

Estimated sum $1 + 3 + 1 = 5$

If you round the first 3 values to the nearest whole number, the sum is 5. Even though $2\frac{5}{6}$ and $\frac{7}{8}$ were rounded up, meaning that $3 + 1$ is greater than the actual sum of $2\frac{5}{6} + \frac{7}{8}$, the $1\frac{1}{3}$ was rounded down to 1. The unused $\frac{1}{3}$ and $\frac{5}{12}$ will compensate for making the other values greater. Here, the estimated sum is less than the actual sum. This means Elaine will have enough lace because the actual sum is greater than 5 yards. The estimate is an underestimate because the adjustment to the actual values (regardless that some were rounded up and others down) results in an estimated sum that is less than the actual sum. By underestimating the actual sum, you can show that there is more lace than needed.

Suggested Question When discussing part (3) of Question C, where students find common denominators and are asked to think about how this is helpful in finding a sum, ask:

- *Why would finding common denominators help you find the actual length of the lace?* (If all the fractions are made with the same size parts it is easy to add up the numerators to see how many parts there are.)

In Question D, parts (1) and (3) are situations where estimating is sensible. Students may argue that it does not make sense to estimate in part (2) because $\frac{2}{3}$ and $\frac{1}{3}$ are one whole. This is a perfectly reasonable argument. Since these are non-contextual problems, either an overestimate or an underestimate will suffice as long as it is reasonable. You can ask students if their estimated sum is an underestimate or an overestimate.

Close the summary by describing an overestimate and an underestimate. Revisit student examples of situations in which an underestimate is needed and some in which an overestimate is needed. This will allow you to assess how well they are making sense of underestimates and overestimates, as well as when they are useful.

Suggested Questions

- *What is an overestimate?* (You are finding an overestimate when the estimated sum is greater than the actual sum.)

- *What are some situations in which you want to overestimate?* (when you are trying to be sure that you will have more than you actually need, to be sure you have enough, when serving food or buying materials to make something, or when deciding how much money you will need to have to buy something or to travel somewhere)

- *What is an underestimate?* (You are underestimating when the estimated sum is less than the actual sum.)

- *For what type of situations are underestimates useful?* (when you want to have "about some amount" and you don't want to have extra, when it is okay to have extra but you need to be sure you have a certain minimum amount, when you are trying to see if you have enough of something and you want to be sure your estimate is less than what you actually need so you can be sure you have enough, or when you are cooking and want to underestimate what is available because this means that you really have more than enough)

1.2 Estimating Sums

Mathematical Goals

- Use estimation skills in contextual situations where an exact answer is not needed to make an informed decision
- Make decisions about whether an overestimate or an underestimate will suffice

Launch

Pose a few non-contextual fraction addition problems to estimate. Discuss that an overestimate occurs when the estimated sum is greater than the actual sum and an underestimate occurs when the estimated sum is less than the actual sum. For example:

- *What is a reasonable estimate for $1\frac{5}{6} + 1\frac{7}{8}$?*
- *Is the estimated sum greater than or less than the actual sum?*
- *Is this an overestimate of the actual sum or an underestimate?*

Discuss any overestimates and underestimates that are reasonable. For example, $2 + 2 = 4$, $1\frac{1}{2} + 1\frac{1}{2} = 3$, and $1\frac{1}{2} + 2 = 3\frac{1}{2}$. Look at the same sum in a contextual situation.

- *What if you are buying fencing for a small garden and the actual lengths you need are $1\frac{5}{6}$ ft and $1\frac{7}{8}$ ft. Which of these three estimates is most useful? Would you want to buy 3 ft, $3\frac{1}{2}$ ft, or 4 ft of fencing? Why?*
- *When working with only numbers, any of these estimates is reasonable. In real-life situations, you often must choose a specific type of estimate.*

Introduce the problem to your students. Use a Think-Pair-Share classroom organization.

Vocabulary
- underestimate (review)
- overestimate (review)

Explore

Observe the types of approaches students are using. Students may need help focusing on the actual sum and the estimated sum.

- *Is the estimated sum greater than (an overestimate of) or less than (an underestimate of) your actual sum?*
- *What does the estimated sum tell you about how much material or lace you need?*

In Question B, focus on questions like the following:

- *What is a reasonable estimate for the amount Madison needs?*
- *Based on the estimate, whose solution is reasonable?*

Have students share their estimates. Ask questions like the following:

- *Is this a situation where you need an underestimate or an overestimate? Why? What is a reasonable estimate that lets you be sure you have enough material? How do you know?*

continued on next page

Materials
• Student notebooks

• *What is an overestimate? What are some situations where it is useful? What is an underestimate, and where is it useful?*

ACE Assignment Guide for Problem 1.2

Differentiated Instruction
Solutions for All Learners

Core 28–30, 37–40
Other *Applications* 26, 27; *Connections* 36, 41, 42; unassigned choices from previous problems

Adapted For suggestions about adapting Exercise 30 and other ACE exercises, see the CMP *Special Needs Handbook*.
Connecting to Prior Units 36–42: *Bits and Pieces I*

Answers to Problem 1.2

A. 1. No, Elaine does not have enough molding.

   2. Possible answers:

     Solution 1: Using $3\frac{1}{4} + 2\frac{1}{4}$, the estimated sum is less than the actual sum. With this estimate you can show that by using less than what you actually need, $5\frac{1}{2}$ is not enough molding because the actual amount she needs is more than $5\frac{1}{2}$.

     Solution 2: If you round $2\frac{3}{8}$ up by $\frac{1}{8}$ and use $2\frac{1}{2}$, $3\frac{1}{4} + 2\frac{1}{2} = 5\frac{3}{4}$. This is $\frac{1}{8}$ more than the actual answer. So, $5\frac{1}{2}$ is not enough.

   3. Solutions will vary. Solution 1 (above) is an underestimate and Solution 2 is an overestimate. (What is important is that students *know* which strategy they are using, and why.)

B. 1. Overestimate. If you underestimate you will not have enough material to make the curtains. You want to overestimate so that you have a little more material than what is needed.

   2. $\frac{7}{12}$ and $\frac{5}{8}$ are both more than $\frac{1}{2}$, so the sum should be more than 1. $\frac{12}{20}$ is less than 1, so it is not a reasonable estimate.

3. a. $\frac{29}{24}$, or $1\frac{5}{24}$. Jamar's answer makes sense if you think of the denominator as how many parts make a whole and the numerator as the number of parts you have. With this reasoning, the fraction parts are all renamed as 24ths so that adding the numerators tells how many 24ths there are in total. Without common denominators, you will be trying to add up quantities with different-sized fractional parts. While you could count how many there are, there is not a consistent single name you could use to label the size of what you have counted.

   b. exact

C. 1. Underestimate. The exact answer is greater than 5 yards, but if you can estimate and show that you have at least 5 yards you don't need to know the actual amount because you know the total is greater than 5 yards.

   2. The whole numbers, 1 and 2, total 3 yards. Both $\frac{1}{3} + \frac{5}{6}$, and $\frac{7}{8} + \frac{5}{12}$, are each more than a whole, so the total is more than 5 yards. She has enough lace.

   3. $1\frac{1}{3} = 1\frac{8}{24}$ $2\frac{5}{6} = 2\frac{20}{24}$ $\frac{7}{8} = \frac{21}{24}$ $\frac{5}{12} = \frac{10}{24}$
Since all the lengths are measured in 24ths, you can add up how many 24ths you have. Combine the number of 24ths with the three wholes for the complete sum, which is $3\frac{59}{24}$, or $5\frac{11}{24}$.

D. 1. $\frac{2}{3} + \frac{1}{5}$ is a little less than 1. If $\frac{1}{3}$ is added to $\frac{2}{3}$, it is equal to 1. Adding $\frac{1}{5}$, which is less than $\frac{1}{3}$, to $\frac{2}{3}$ will make the sum less than 1.

   2. $2\frac{1}{3} + 3\frac{2}{3} = 6$; Students may estimate, but this is a problem where an estimate does not really make sense. Finding the exact answer is simple enough to do.

   3. $\frac{3}{4} + \frac{4}{3}$ is about 2 because $\frac{3}{4}$ is a little less than 1, and $\frac{4}{3}$ is 1 whole plus $\frac{1}{3}$, or a little more than 1. Together this is about 2.

Investigation 1

Estimating With Fractions

Sometimes when you need to find an amount, you do not need an exact answer. In these situations, making a reasonable estimate of the answer is good enough. This investigation will help you develop strategies for estimating sums and differences. The sums and differences will involve fractions, as well as decimals.

1.1 Getting Close

Getting Close is a game that will sharpen your estimating skills. In *Bits and Pieces I*, you used *benchmarks* to estimate fractions and decimals. Look at this set of benchmarks.

$$0 \quad \frac{1}{4} \quad \frac{1}{2} \quad \frac{3}{4} \quad 1 \quad 1\frac{1}{4} \quad 1\frac{1}{2} \quad 1\frac{3}{4} \quad 2$$

Which benchmark is $\frac{3}{8}$ nearest? Three-eighths is less than $\frac{1}{2}$, because it is less than $\frac{4}{8}$. Three-eighths is greater than $\frac{1}{4}$, because it is greater than $\frac{2}{8}$. In fact, $\frac{3}{8}$ is exactly halfway between $\frac{1}{4}$ and $\frac{1}{2}$.

Which benchmark is 0.58 nearest? Since $\frac{1}{2}$ is equal to 0.50, 0.58 is greater than $\frac{1}{2}$. You also know that 0.58 is less than $\frac{3}{4}$ or 0.75. So 0.58 is between $\frac{1}{2}$ and $\frac{3}{4}$, but it is closer to $\frac{1}{2}$.

Investigation 1 Estimating With Fractions **5**

Notes _____

_____

_____

_____

How can you use benchmarks to help you estimate the sum of two fractions? Think about the example below.

$$\frac{1}{2} + \frac{5}{8}$$

- Is the sum between 0 and 1 or between 1 and 2?
- Is the sum closest to 0, to 1, or to 2?

When you play the Getting Close game, you will use benchmarks and other strategies to estimate the sum of two numbers.

Getting Close Rules

Two to four players can play Getting Close.

Materials

- Getting Close game cards (one set per group)
- A set of four number squares (0, 1, 2, and 3) for each player

Playing

1. All players hold their 0, 1, 2, and 3 number squares in their hand.

2. The cards are placed face-down in a pile in the center of the table.

3. One player turns over two game cards from the pile. Each player mentally estimates the sum of the numbers on the two game cards. Each player then selects from their set the number square (0, 1, 2, or 3) closest to their estimate and places it face-down on the table.

4. After each player has played a number square, the players turn their number squares over at the same time.

5. The player whose number square is closest to the actual sum gets the two game cards. If there is a tie, all players who tied get one game card. Players who have tied may take a game card from the deck if necessary.

6. Players take turns turning over the two game cards.

7. When all cards have been used, the player with the most cards wins.

6 Bits and Pieces II

Notes _____

_____

_____

_____

You may find benchmarks, fraction strips, number lines, diagrams, or changing a fraction to a decimal helpful in making estimates. You may discover other ways of thinking that help as well.

Problem 1.1 Using Benchmarks

Play Getting Close several times. Keep a record of the estimation strategies you find useful.

A. 1. Describe or illustrate one estimation strategy that you found useful in the game.

2. For which pairs was it easy and for which pairs was it hard to estimate the sum? Why?

B. Suppose you played Getting Close with only these game cards:

1. What is the greatest sum possible with any two of the game cards shown?

2. What is the least sum possible with any two of the game cards shown?

ACE Homework starts on page 10.

Notes _____

_____

_____

_____

1.2 Estimating Sums

In this problem, you will see several situations that use fractions and involve estimating sums. There are times when you should overestimate what is needed to make sure you have enough. Other times, you want to underestimate to make sure you do not take or assume too much.

Problem 1.2 Estimating Sums

A. Elaine is making a model of a house that she designed. She wants to put wood molding around two rooms in the model. She measures and finds that she needs $3\frac{1}{4}$ feet of molding for one room and $2\frac{3}{8}$ feet of molding for the other room. She has $5\frac{1}{2}$ feet of molding.

  1. Estimate whether she has enough molding.

  2. Describe your strategy for estimating the answer.

  3. Is your estimate an overestimate or an underestimate of the sum?

Notes _____

_____

_____

_____

B. Elaine asks her granddaughter, Madison, to make curtains for the windows in the two model rooms. The pattern for the first room calls for a $\frac{7}{12}$-yard strip of material. The pattern for the second room calls for a $\frac{5}{8}$-yard strip.

1. Should Madison underestimate or overestimate the amount of material she needs? Why?

2. She writes the following computation: $\frac{7}{12} + \frac{5}{8} = \frac{12}{20}$. Use estimation to check whether her computation is reasonable. Explain your thinking.

3. Madison's friend, Jamar, says that he can write $\frac{7}{12} + \frac{5}{8}$ using the same denominator. He writes $\frac{14}{24} + \frac{15}{24}$ and says, "Now the answer is easy."

   a. What do you think Jamar will give as the sum? Does his thinking make sense?

   b. Is this an exact answer or an estimate?

C. Elaine makes the lace edging that is used to decorate the curtains in the model house. She needs 5 yards of lace for the curtains. She has these lengths of lace on hand:

   $1\frac{1}{3}$ yards $\qquad$ $2\frac{5}{6}$ yards $\qquad$ $\frac{7}{8}$ yard $\qquad$ $\frac{5}{12}$ yard

1. Should Elaine underestimate or overestimate the amount of lace she has? Why?

2. Use estimation to tell whether she has enough lace.

3. Find equivalent fractions with the same denominator to represent the lengths of lace. How does this help you find the actual length of all the lace?

D. Estimate these sums and describe your thinking.

   1. $\frac{2}{3} + \frac{1}{5}$ $\qquad\qquad$ **2.** $2\frac{1}{3} + 3\frac{2}{3}$ $\qquad\qquad$ **3.** $\frac{3}{4} + \frac{4}{3}$

ACE Homework starts on page 10.

Investigation 1 Estimating With Fractions $\qquad$ **9**

Notes _____

_____

_____

_____

Applications

For Exercises 1–9, determine whether the number is closest to $0, \frac{1}{2}$, or 1. Explain your reasoning.

1. $\frac{10}{9}$

2. $\frac{9}{16}$

3. $\frac{2}{15}$

4. $\frac{500}{1000}$

5. $\frac{5}{6}$

6. $\frac{48}{100}$

7. 0.67

8. 0.26

9. 0.0009999

For Exercises 10–15, determine whether the sum of the two Getting Close game cards is closest to 0, 1, 2, or 3. Explain.

10. $\frac{7}{8}$ and $\frac{4}{9}$

11. $1\frac{4}{10}$ and 0.375

12. $\frac{2}{5}$ and $\frac{7}{10}$

13. $1\frac{3}{4}$ and $\frac{1}{8}$

14. $1\frac{1}{3}$ and 1.3

15. 0.25 and $\frac{1}{8}$

For Exercises 16–18, you are playing a game called Getting Even Closer. In this game, you have to estimate sums to the nearest $\frac{1}{2}$, or 0.5. Decide if the sum of the two game cards turned up is closest to $0, \frac{1}{2}$, or 1. Explain.

16. $\frac{3}{5}$ and $\frac{1}{10}$

17. $\frac{1}{4}$ and $\frac{1}{10}$

18. $\frac{1}{9}$ and $\frac{1}{8}$

19. Four students were asked the following question: "Can you find two fractions with a sum greater than $\frac{3}{4}$?" Explain whether each student's answer below is correct.

a. $\frac{1}{8} + \frac{2}{4}$

b. $\frac{3}{6} + \frac{2}{4}$

c. $\frac{5}{12} + \frac{5}{6}$

d. $\frac{5}{10} + \frac{3}{8}$

Homework Help Online
PHSchool.com
For: Help with Exercise 19
Web Code: ame-4119

For Exercises 20–25, find two fractions with a sum that is between the two given numbers.

20. 0 and $\frac{1}{2}$

21. $\frac{1}{2}$ and 1

22. 1 and $1\frac{1}{2}$

23. $1\frac{1}{2}$ and 2

24. 2 and $2\frac{1}{2}$

25. $2\frac{1}{2}$ and 3

26. Many sewing patterns have a $\frac{5}{8}$-inch border for sewing the seam. Is a $\frac{5}{8}$-inch border closest to $0, \frac{1}{2}$, or 1 inch? Explain.

10 Bits and Pieces II

STUDENT PAGE

Notes _____

_____

_____

_____

27. Last season Farmer Sam picked $1\frac{3}{4}$ bushels of tomatoes from his kitchen garden and $14\frac{1}{3}$ bushels from his canning garden. About how many total bushels of tomatoes did he harvest?

28. Suppose you mix $\frac{5}{8}$ cup of wheat flour with $1\frac{3}{4}$ cups of white flour. Do you have enough for a recipe that calls for $2\frac{1}{2}$ cups of flour?

29. Soo needs 2 yards of molding to put around the bottom of a stand. He has two pieces of molding: one is $\frac{7}{8}$ yard long and the other is $\frac{8}{7}$ yard long. Estimate whether he has enough molding. Explain.

Go Online
PHSchool.com
For: Multiple-Choice Skills
Practice
Web Code: ama-4154

30. Julio is at the grocery store. He has $10.00. Here is a list of the items he would like to buy. Use mental computation and estimation to answer parts (a)–(c).

Milk	$2.47
Eggs	$1.09
Cheese	$1.95
Bread	$0.68
Honey	$1.19
Cereal	$3.25
Avocado	$0.50
Chipotles	$1.29

a. Can Julio buy all the items with the money he has? Explain.

b. If he has only $5.00, what can he buy? Give two possibilities.

c. What different items can Julio buy to come as close as possible to spending $5.00?

Investigation 1 Estimating With Fractions **11**

Notes _____

_____

_____

_____

Connections

31. The rectangle shown represents $\frac{3}{4}$ of a whole.

    a. Draw a rectangle representing the whole.

    b. Draw a rectangle representing $\frac{5}{4}$ of the whole.

32. The rectangle shown represents 150% of a whole. Draw 100% of the same whole.

33. The beans shown represent $\frac{3}{5}$ of the total beans on the kitchen counter. How many total beans are there on the counter?

34. The following fractions occur so often in our lives that it is useful to quickly recall their decimal and percent equivalents.

$$\frac{1}{2} \quad \frac{1}{3} \quad \frac{1}{4} \quad \frac{2}{3} \quad \frac{3}{4} \quad \frac{1}{6} \quad \frac{1}{5} \quad \frac{1}{8}$$

    a. For each of these important fractions, give the decimal and percent equivalents.

    b. Draw a number line. On your number line, mark the point that corresponds to each fraction shown above. Label each point with its fraction, decimal, and percent equivalent.

12 Bits and Pieces II

Notes _____

_____

_____

_____

35. Multiple Choice Choose the set of decimals that is ordered from least to greatest.

   A. 5.603 5.63 5.096 5.67 5.599

   B. 5.63 5.67 5.096 5.599 5.603

   C. 5.096 5.63 5.67 5.603 5.599

   D. 5.096 5.599 5.603 5.63 5.67

36. In which of the following groups of fractions can *all* the fractions be renamed as a whole number of hundredths? Explain your reasoning for each.

   a. $\frac{3}{2}, \frac{3}{4}, \frac{3}{5}$ **b.** $\frac{7}{10}, \frac{7}{11}, \frac{7}{12}$

   c. $\frac{2}{5}, \frac{2}{6}, \frac{2}{8}$ **d.** $\frac{11}{5}, \frac{11}{10}, \frac{11}{20}$

For Exercises 37–40, copy the figure onto your paper. Then, divide the figure into fourths. Shade $\frac{1}{4}$ of the figure.

37.

38.

39.

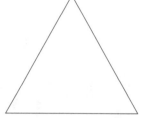

40.

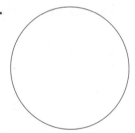

Investigation 1 Estimating With Fractions   **13**

Notes _____

_____

_____

_____

In Exercises 41 and 42, craft paint has spilled on the page, covering part of the fraction strips. Use what is showing to reason about each pair of strips. Find the equivalent fractions indicated by the question marks.

41.

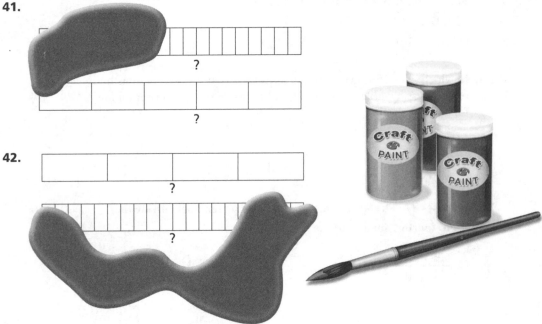

42.

Extensions

For Exercises 43–46, name a fraction in the given interval.

43. between $\frac{1}{3}$ and $\frac{1}{2}$

44. between $\frac{1}{4}$ and $\frac{1}{3}$

45. between $\frac{1}{5}$ and $\frac{1}{4}$

46. between $\frac{1}{6}$ and $\frac{1}{5}$

47. In Exercises 43–46, is it possible to find another fraction in each interval? Why or why not?

Notes _____

_____

_____

_____

Mathematical Reflections 1

In this investigation, you developed strategies for estimating the sum of fractions and decimals. These questions will help you to summarize what you have learned.

Think about your answers to these questions. Discuss your ideas with other students and your teacher. Then write a summary of your findings in your notebook.

1. Describe at least two strategies for estimating fraction sums. Give an example for each strategy. Explain how each strategy is useful.

2. How do you decide whether an overestimate or an underestimate is most helpful? Give examples to help explain your thinking.

Investigation 1 Estimating With Fractions   **15**

Notes _____

_____

_____

_____

Investigation 1

ACE Assignment Choices

Differentiated Instruction
Solutions for All Learners

Problem 1.1
Core 1–15, 19–22, 31–33, 35
Other *Applications* 16–18, 23–25; *Connections* 34; *Extensions* 43–47

Problem 1.2
Core 28–30, 37–40
Other *Applications* 26, 27; *Connections* 36, 41, 42; unassigned choices from previous problems

Adapted For suggestions about adapting Exercise 30 and other ACE exercises, see the CMP *Special Needs Handbook*.
Connecting to Prior Units 31–42: *Bits and Pieces 1*

Applications

1. 1; Possible explanation: $\frac{9}{9}$ is 1, so $\frac{10}{9}$ is more than 1.

2. $\frac{1}{2}$; Possible explanation: Since $\frac{8}{16} = \frac{1}{2}$, $\frac{9}{16}$ is close to $\frac{1}{2}$.

3. 0; Possible explanation: $\frac{1}{2}$ of 15 is $7\frac{1}{2}$. Two is closer to 0 than to $7\frac{1}{2}$, so $\frac{2}{15}$ is closer to 0 than to $\frac{1}{2}$.

4. $\frac{1}{2}$; Possible explanation: 500 is exactly half of 1000.

5. 1; Possible explanation: $\frac{5}{6}$ is only $\frac{1}{6}$ less than 1 whole.

6. $\frac{1}{2}$; Possible explanation: $\frac{1}{2}$ of 100 is 50, so $\frac{48}{100}$ is closer to $\frac{1}{2}$.

7. $\frac{1}{2}$; Possible explanation: $\frac{1}{2}$ is 0.50 and $\frac{3}{4}$ is 0.75, so 0.67 is closer to $\frac{1}{2}$.

8. $\frac{1}{2}$; 0.25 would be exactly $\frac{1}{2}$ of a $\frac{1}{2}$, or $\frac{1}{2}$ of 0.50. 0.26 is a little more than 0.25, so it is closer to $\frac{1}{2}$ than to 0.

9. 0; Possible explanation: 0.0009999 is a very small amount. It does not have any tenths in it, and $\frac{1}{2}$ is equivalent to 5 tenths.

10. 1; Possible explanation: $\frac{7}{8}$ is a little less than 1 and $\frac{4}{9}$ is a little less than $\frac{1}{2}$. Together, a little less than 1 and a little less than $\frac{1}{2}$ is a little less than $1\frac{1}{2}$, or closer to 1 than to 2.

11. 2; Possible explanation: 0.375 is a little less than 0.4, or $\frac{4}{10}$. Together, $1\frac{4}{10}$ and about $\frac{4}{10}$ is about $1\frac{8}{10}$, which is close to 2.

12. 1; Possible explanation: $\frac{2}{5} = \frac{4}{10} \cdot \frac{4}{10}$ and $\frac{7}{10}$ is $\frac{11}{10}$, or a little more than 1.

13. 2; Possible explanation: $1\frac{3}{4} = 1\frac{6}{8} \cdot 1\frac{6}{8}$ and $\frac{1}{8}$ is $1\frac{7}{8}$, or a little less than 2.

14. 3; Possible explanation: $1\frac{1}{3}$ is a little more than 1.3. 1.3 and 1.3 is 2.6, which is greater than $2\frac{1}{2}$, and closest to 3.

15. 0; Possible explanation: It would take two $\frac{1}{4}$'s to equal exactly $\frac{1}{2}$. Since $\frac{1}{8}$ is less than $\frac{1}{4}$, $\frac{1}{4}$ and $\frac{1}{8}$ is less than $\frac{1}{2}$ and closer to 0.

16. $\frac{1}{2}$; Possible explanation: $\frac{3}{5}$ is equivalent to $\frac{6}{10}$. $\frac{6}{10}$ and $\frac{1}{10}$ is $\frac{7}{10}$, which is closer to $\frac{1}{2}$ than to 1.

17. $\frac{1}{2}$; Possible explanation: If you think of the fractions as money, then you have 0.25 and 0.10, or a quarter and a dime, which is 35 cents. 0.35 closer to $\frac{1}{2}$ than to 0.

18. 0; Possible explanation: Each fraction is less than $\frac{1}{7}$, and $\frac{2}{7}$ would be closer to 0 than to $\frac{1}{2}$.

19. Choices (b), (c), and (d) are correct because the sums are greater than $\frac{3}{4}$. Choice (a) is less than $\frac{3}{4}$. Explanations will vary.

20. Possible answer: $\frac{1}{4}$ and $\frac{1}{7}$

21. Possible answer: $\frac{3}{8}$ and $\frac{4}{9}$

22. Possible answer: $\frac{5}{8}$ and $\frac{1}{2}$

23. Possible answer: $\frac{5}{6}$ and $\frac{7}{8}$

24. Possible answer: $1\frac{3}{4}$ and $\frac{3}{8}$

25. Possible answer: $1\frac{9}{10}$ and $\frac{15}{16}$

26. $\frac{5}{8}$ is closest to $\frac{1}{2}$. Possible explanation: $\frac{4}{8} = \frac{1}{2}$. The other $\frac{1}{8}$ makes $\frac{5}{8}$ just a little more than $\frac{1}{2}$, but not close to $\frac{8}{8}$, or 1 whole.

27. About 16 bushels. $14 + 1 = 15$ bushels and $\frac{3}{4} + \frac{1}{3}$ is about 1 more bushel.

28. No; If you add $\frac{3}{4}$ to $1\frac{3}{4}$, you will get $2\frac{1}{2}$. But $\frac{5}{8}$ is a little less than $\frac{3}{4}$, so there is not enough.

29. Soo has enough molding. $\frac{7}{8}$ is $\frac{1}{8}$ less than 1 whole and $\frac{8}{7}$ is $\frac{1}{7}$ more than 1 whole, or $1\frac{1}{7}$. Since $\frac{1}{7} > \frac{1}{8}$, when the $\frac{1}{7}$ is added to the $\frac{7}{8}$ it will be greater than 1 yard, and the total will be greater than 2 yards.

30. a. No; In the price list, the whole numbers add up to 9: $2 + 1 + 1 + 1 + 3 + 1 = 9$. The cheese is $1.95, which brings the total to $9.95. There's clearly enough in the cost of other items to put the total over $10. (The exact cost of the groceries is $12.42.)

   b. Possible answers: Milk, cheese, avocado ($4.92); eggs, cheese, honey, bread ($4.91)

   c. Cereal, honey, and avocado ($4.94)

Connections

31. a.

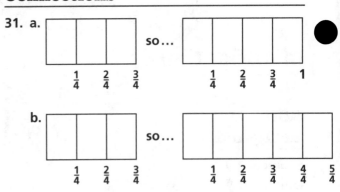

b.

32.

so...

50% 100% 150%   50% 100%

33. 15 beans. There are 9 beans shown in the picture representing three fifths. So each fifth must contain 3 beans. Since the whole is five fifths, there must be 15 beans on the counter.

34. a. $\frac{1}{2}$ is 0.5 and 50%

   $\frac{1}{3}$ is about 0.33 and 33%

   $\frac{1}{4}$ is 0.25 and 25%

   $\frac{2}{3}$ is about 0.66 and or 66% (Some students will argue for 0.67 and 67%, if the convention of rounding up is used.)

   $\frac{3}{4}$ is 0.75 and 75%

   $\frac{1}{6}$ is about 0.16 and 16% (Some students will argue for 0.17 and 17%, if the convention of rounding up is used.)

   $\frac{1}{5}$ is 0.2 or 20%

   $\frac{1}{8}$ is 0.125 or 12.5%

   b. (Figure 1)

35. D

Figure 1

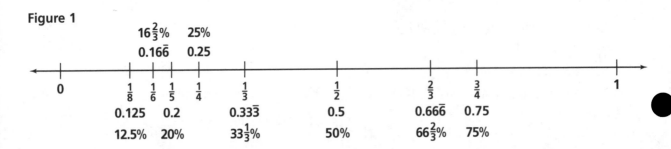

36. a. This set of fractions can easily be renamed as hundredths because each denominator, 2, 4, and 5, are factors of 100.

b. This set of fractions cannot easily be renamed as hundredths. The denominator 10 is a factor of 100, but 11 and 12 are not.

c. This set of fractions cannot be easily renamed as hundredths. The denominators 6 and 8 are not factors of 100.

d. This set of fractions can easily be renamed as hundredths because all the denominators, 5, 10, and 20, are factors of 100.

37. Possible answer:

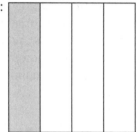

38. Possible answer:

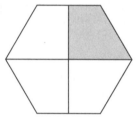

39. Possible answer:

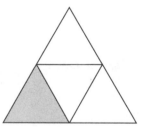

40. Possible answer:

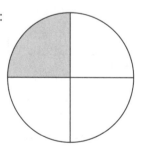

41. $\frac{3}{5} = \frac{12}{20}$

42. $\frac{2}{4} = \frac{10}{20}$

Extensions

43. Possible answers: $\frac{4}{10}, \frac{2}{5}, \frac{49}{100}, \frac{5}{12}$

44. Possible answers: $\frac{3}{10}, \frac{31}{100}, \frac{13}{50}, \frac{7}{24}$

45. Possible answers: $\frac{21}{100}, \frac{22}{100}, \frac{11}{50}, \frac{9}{40}$

46. Possible answers: $\frac{17}{100}, \frac{185}{1000}, \frac{9}{50}, \frac{11}{60}$

47. Yes; Possible explanation: There are lots of numbers in each of the intervals. If you make equivalent fractions with the same, but larger, denominator, you can look for fractions between the ones you have.

Possible Answers to Mathematical Reflections

1. One strategy is to use benchmarks such as 0, $\frac{1}{2}$, and 1. First, decide which benchmark each number is closest to, and then add the two benchmark estimates together. For example, $\frac{3}{5} + 1\frac{1}{12}$ is approximately $\frac{1}{2} + 1 = 1\frac{1}{2}$. Another strategy involves using unit fractions to determine how far a fraction is away from a benchmark. For example, in the problem $\frac{5}{6} + \frac{1}{9} = \blacksquare$, $\frac{5}{6}$ is $\frac{1}{6}$ less than 1 whole and $\frac{1}{9}$ is less than $\frac{1}{6}$. So $\frac{5}{6} + \frac{1}{9}$ will be a little less than 1.

2. An overestimate is most helpful when you have to be sure you have enough of something and having less than what is needed will not work. For example, when buying wallpaper you would not want to underestimate and not have enough wallpaper to cover the wall. Here rounding values up will insure that you have more than you need.

An underestimate is most helpful when you need to have "about" some amount and you don't want to have extra. If you are a little short, it is okay. An underestimate is also useful to make when you are trying to see if you have at least enough of something. For example if you need 5 cups of something and you round all your values down and realize you have 5 cups, then you have underestimated what you actually have, but can be sure you have enough.

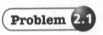

Investigation 2 — Adding and Subtracting Fractions

Mathematical and Problem-Solving Goals

- Use number sentences to express sums and differences
- Explore the use of fractions as operators (e.g., $\frac{2}{3}$ of 640 acres)
- Write number sentences to represent situations for adding and subtracting fractions and mixed numbers
- Explore the inverse relationship between the addition and subtraction of fractions
- Develop and use efficient strategies for adding and subtracting fractions and mixed numbers
- Develop an efficient algorithm for adding and subtracting fractions

Summary of Problems

Problem 2.1 Land Sections: Writing Addition and Subtraction Sentences

Students use an area model in the context of buying and selling land to reason about how to add and subtract fractions.

Problem 2.2 Visiting the Spice Shop: Using Addition and Subtraction

Students continue to work on addition and subtraction, using spice recipes as a context.

Problem 2.3 Just the Facts

Students use fact families to explore the relationship between addition and subtraction.

Problem 2.4 Designing Algorithms for Addition and Subtraction

Students encounter addition and subtraction problems grouped into categories based on how they are solved. Students are asked to decide what each group has in common and then write an efficient algorithm for adding and subtracting fractions.

Mathematics Background

For background on developing algorithms and addition and subtraction, see pages 4–6.

	Suggested Pacing	Materials for Students	Materials for Teachers	ACE Assignments
All	$5\frac{1}{2}$ days	Calculators, colored pens, pencils, or markers; student notebooks	Blank transparencies and transparency markers	
2.1	$1\frac{1}{2}$ days	Labsheet 2.1 (1 per student plus extras; you can copy the blackline master on both sides of paper); Labsheet 2ACE Exercise 1	Transparency 2.1	1, 2, 28, 29
2.2	1 day	Labsheet 2.2 (1 per student)	Transparency 2.2	3–13, 30–38, 48, 51
2.3	1 day			14–18, 39–44, 49
2.4	$1\frac{1}{2}$ days	Large chart paper or blank transparency film, markers	Transparencies 2.4A and 2.4B	19–27, 45–47, 50
MR	$\frac{1}{2}$ day			

2.1 Land Sections: Writing Addition and Subtraction Sentences

Goals

- Use number sentences to express sums and differences

- Develop strategies for adding and subtracting fractions

- Explore the use of fractions as operators (e.g. $\frac{2}{3}$ of 640 acres)

This problem engages students with an area model for fractions. The students are first asked to name what fraction of a section each person owns. Next students explore combining and removing parts of the section. In addition, each section is equivalent to 640 acres. This allows for questions that show the relative size of parts of the sections in another way—number of acres owned.

In this investigation and the ones that follow, students will be asked to write number (or mathematical) sentences to represent and symbolize situations. During the explore phase of the lesson, pay attention to the students' notation in their work. The summary is also an opportunity to help the students make a connection between their mental computations and number sentences that symbolize what they have done.

Mathematics Background

For background on writing number sentences, see page 4.

Launch 2.1

Before starting Problem 2.1, use the introduction to Investigation 2 in the Student Edition to review what a number sentence is. Make the students aware that there are several names that will be used to indicate that they are to write a number sentence. These might include: mathematical sentence, addition sentence, subtraction sentence, multiplication sentence, and division sentence.

Suggested Questions One way to launch the problem is to have a conversation with your students about naming amounts with fractions. Pose questions like the following:

- *How many sections of land are being discussed in this problem?* (2)

- *How many acres are in a section?* (640)

- *Does anyone own a whole section?* (No. That means everyone owns a fraction that is less than 1.)

- *Who owns the largest piece of a section?* (Maybe Foley or Walker.)

- *About how much does Foley own?* (Between $\frac{1}{4}$ and $\frac{1}{2}$ of a section, maybe $\frac{1}{3}$.)

- *About how much does Burg own?* (A little less than $\frac{1}{4}$ of a section, maybe $\frac{1}{5}$.)

- *What would be a reasonable estimate for Burg + Foley?* (about $\frac{1}{2}$)

- *How much land does Lapp own?* ($\frac{1}{4}$)

- *What do you think it means in Question B when it says to write a number sentence? Can you give an example?* (Students will not know the exact fractional values, but you can use words to write a model and explain that they will replace the words with fractions once they figure out what these values are. For example: Fuentes + Theule = ■.)

Provide students with a copy of Labsheet 2.1. Extra copies of the map are recommended for students who go off in the wrong direction and are too far along to restart on the same sheet. This problem works well in a Think-Pair-Share arrangement. Give the students time to tackle the problem themselves before they share with a partner or a larger group.

Explore 2.1

You may want to check that students have accurately labeled the sections in Question A before they go on to use those values in the rest of the problem. Help students who are struggling to write number sentences. It is often helpful for students to write a number sentence with the names of the landowners, and then substitute numerical values. For example,

Bouck + Lapp = Foley is $\frac{1}{16} + \frac{1}{4} = \frac{5}{16}$.

If groups get done early, you can have them show their solution on a transparency of the property map so that it can be shared easily with the class during the summary.

Summarize 2.1

Start the summary by asking the students to discuss how they found the fractions that represent each person's part of land. Any group who did their work on a transparency of the map could show their work and discuss the strategy they used. It is not uncommon to have many different, but equivalent values for each person's share of land.

Suggested Questions Depending on the strategy that students use, several equivalent fractions may be offered for the same landowner. Help students reconcile the different fractions.

- *How did you get $\frac{1}{4}$ for Lapp's part of Section 18?* (If you divide the section into four parts, you can see that Lapp takes up one of the parts.)

- *Did anyone get other fractions for Lapp's part of Section 18?*

- *Lisa said that Lapp owned $\frac{1}{4}$ of Section 18 and Heidi said Lapp owned $\frac{16}{64}$ of Section 18. Who is correct? Why?* (Both are correct. The fractions are equivalent. Students may use diagrams to show this or they may talk about renaming fractions as proof that they are equivalent.)

The summary should include an exploration of the strategies that students use to combine quantities. Have students talk about why their number sentences make sense. Continue to emphasize the role of equivalence when discussing the number sentences that students wrote. This provides another chance to help students focus on the power of equivalent representation of fractions and on the area model for fractions. The reasoning that is required is important to understand the computations.

Here is a conversation that took part in a classroom when talking about Question C.

Classroom Dialogue Model

Teacher *Would one group begin by sharing a number sentence they wrote for Question C and explain why it makes sense?*

Cody *We did Section 19 + Lapp + Gardella + Bouck = $1\frac{1}{2}$. For the number sentence, we wrote $1 + \frac{1}{4} + \frac{3}{16} + \frac{1}{16} = 1\frac{1}{2}$.*

Teacher *How do you know those equal $1\frac{1}{2}$?*

Cody *If you look at the map, you can fit Bouck's land into the upper right corner of Gardella's section. This will fill up half of Section 18.*

Trista *We used the same people but wrote the number sentence $1 + \frac{4}{16} + \frac{3}{16} + \frac{1}{16} = 1\frac{8}{16} = 1\frac{1}{2}$. If you rename Lapp's $\frac{1}{4}$ as $\frac{4}{16}$, it is easy to add the 16ths and get $\frac{8}{16}$ or $\frac{1}{2}$.*

Teacher *How do you know that $\frac{1}{4}$ equals $\frac{4}{16}$?*

Charlie *Because we know that if you multiply or divide the numerator and denominator by the same number you get an equivalent fraction. For $\frac{1}{4}$, we multiplied the numerator and denominator by 4 to get $\frac{4}{16}$.*

Cody *Why did you do that?*

Anne *Well, the denominators tell us the sizes of the pieces, and because the denominators are the same, we know that for these two fractions, the sizes of the pieces are the same. But we have different amounts of pieces, because the numerators are different, and it is the numerators that tell us how many pieces we have. So, with all the pieces in 16ths, we can easily add the number of pieces and see how many 16ths there are.*

Teacher *So your strategy was to use equivalent fractions to rename the pieces with the same denominators so the pieces were the same size and you could easily tell how many there were all together?*

Anne *Yes, it is easy to add up each person's land when the fractions have the same denominator.*

After a group has presented their strategy, ask the class questions like the following:

- *What do others think about this group's strategy? Does it seem reasonable?*

- *Did anyone have a different answer or use a different strategy?*

As you move into the additional parts of the problem, be sure to have students share their number sentences.

Have a few students show their strategies for solving Question E. Here we are foreshadowing multiplication with fractions by having students find a fraction of a number other than 1. This is in contrast to their work in Question A where they found a fractional part of a whole (1).

Question F is a practice problem and can be assigned as homework if time is short. Note that this is an important problem to discuss. This problem uses situations where subtraction may be a useful strategy. For students who do use subtraction, ask them how they would write a number sentence to show their solution.

Suggested Questions

- *How do you decide if addition or subtraction will help solve a problem?*

- *What strategies help you add or subtract fractions?*

2.1 Writing Addition and Subtraction Sentences

Mathematical Goals

- Use number sentences to express sums and differences
- Develop strategies for adding and subtracting fractions
- Explore the use of fractions as operators (e.g., $\frac{2}{3}$ of 640 acres)

Launch

Use the introduction to Investigation 2 in the Student Edition to review number sentences. Read Problem 2.1.

- *How many sections of land are being discussed in this problem?*
- *Does anyone own a whole section?*
- *Who owns the largest piece of a section?*
- *What do you think it means in Question B when it says to write a number sentence? Can you give an example?*

Provide a copy of Labsheet 2.1. Use a Think-Pair-Share grouping arrangement.

Materials
- Transparency 2.1
- Labsheet 2.1 (1 per student but have extra copies for students who need to start again)

Vocabulary
- number sentence

Explore

You may want to check that students have accurately labeled the sections in Question A before they go on to use those values in the rest of Problem 2.1. It is helpful for students to write number sentences with the names of the landowners, and then substitute numerical values. You might have groups put their solutions on a transparency of the property map to share in the summary.

Summarize

As students share their solutions for Questions A–D, ask questions like the following:

- *How did you get $\frac{1}{4}$ for Lapp?*
- *Did anyone get other fractions for Lapp's part of Section 18?*
- *Lisa said that Lapp owned $\frac{1}{4}$ of Section 18, and Heidi said that Lapp owned $\frac{16}{64}$ of Section 18. Who is correct? Why?*

As students share strategies, have them talk about why their number sentences make sense. Continue to emphasize the role of equivalence when adding and subtracting fractions.

- *How do you know that those values together equal $1\frac{1}{2}$?*
- *What do others think about this group's strategy?*

Materials
- Student notebooks

continued on next page

• *Did anyone have a different answer or use a different strategy?*

Question E foreshadows multiplication with fractions by having students find a fraction of a number other than 1.

Question F is practice and can be assigned as homework. Note that this is an important problem to discuss.

• *How do you decide if a problem is addition or subtraction?*

• *What strategies help you add or subtract fractions?*

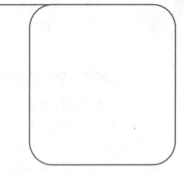

ACE Assignment Guide for Problem 2.1

Differentiated Instruction
Solutions for All Learners

Core 2, 29
Other *Applications* 1, *Connections* 28
Labsheet 2ACE Exercise 1 is provided if Exercise 1 is assigned.

Adapted For suggestions about adapting ACE exercises, see the CMP *Special Needs Handbook*.

Answers to Problem 2.1

A. Lapp: $\frac{1}{4}$; Bouck: $\frac{1}{16}$; Wong: $\frac{3}{32}$; Stewart: $\frac{5}{32}$; Krebs: $\frac{1}{32}$; Fitz: $\frac{5}{32}$; Gardella: $\frac{3}{16}$; Fuentes: $\frac{1}{16}$; Foley: $\frac{5}{16}$; Theule: $\frac{3}{16}$; Burg: $\frac{3}{16}$; Walker: $\frac{5}{16}$.

B. Fuentes + Theule = $\frac{4}{16}$; $\frac{1}{16} + \frac{3}{16} = \frac{4}{16}$

C. **1.** Possible answers: All of section 19 + Lapp + Gardella + Bouck, or $1 + \frac{4}{16} + \frac{3}{16} + \frac{1}{16} = 1\frac{1}{2}$;
All of section 18 + Foley + Theule, or $1 + \frac{5}{16} + \frac{3}{16} = 1\frac{1}{2}$.

2. See part (1).

D. **1.** $\frac{1}{16} + \frac{1}{4} = \frac{5}{16}$. To show this is true, you can rewrite Lapp's section as $\frac{4}{16}$.
$\frac{1}{16} + \frac{4}{16} = \frac{5}{16}$.

2. Possible answer: Bouck + Wong = Stewart or $\frac{1}{16} + \frac{3}{32} = \frac{5}{32}$.

3. Possible answer: Burg + Fuentes + Bouck = Walker or $\frac{3}{16} + \frac{1}{16} + \frac{1}{16} = \frac{5}{16}$.

E. Lapp: 160 acres; Bouck: 40 acres; Wong: 60 acres; Stewart: 100 acres; Krebs: 20 acres; Fitz: 100 acres; Gardella: 120 acres; Fuentes: 40 acres; Foley: 200 acres; Theule: 120 acres; Burg: 120 acres; Walker: 200 acres
Possible explanation: Each section can be broken into 32 parts, so each part is 20 acres. Then Lapp has 8 of the 32 parts, or 160 acres; Bouck has 2 parts, or 40 acres; Wong has 3 parts, or 60 acres; and so on.

F. **1.** $\frac{21}{32}$; Lapp + Gardella + Fuentes + Fitz = $\frac{1}{4} + \frac{3}{16} + \frac{1}{16} + \frac{5}{32} = \frac{21}{32}$

2. $\frac{11}{32}$; Wong + Stewart + Krebs + Bouck = $\frac{3}{32} + \frac{5}{32} + \frac{1}{32} + \frac{1}{16} = \frac{11}{32}$, or $1 - \frac{21}{32} = \frac{11}{32}$

3. Lapp by $\frac{10}{32}$; $\frac{21}{32} - \frac{11}{32} = \frac{10}{32}$

2.2 Visiting the Spice Shop: Using Addition and Subtraction

Goals

- Write number sentences to represent situations for adding and subtracting fractions and mixed numbers

- Develop strategies for adding and subtracting fractions and mixed numbers

Questions A–C of Problem 2.2 use the context of mixing spices. Questions D and E ask students to stand back and make explicit use of what they have been learning about computational strategies for adding and subtracting mixed numbers with non-contextual problems.

As students work, they should come to realize that they need fractions with common denominators in order to add and subtract fractional quantities. When mixed numbers are involved, students may operate on the whole numbers and the fractions separately. While the traditional addition and subtraction algorithm expects students to operate on fractions first and whole numbers second, many students prefer to operate on the whole numbers first followed by the fractions. Allow students to work in either direction.

Parts (5) and (6) of Question D are missing-value problems. These kinds of problems will appear throughout the unit. The goal is to introduce students to variable notation where the variable is being used as a placeholder. In addition, we want students to explore the role of inverse operations so they have experience with this type of reasoning and can draw upon it in future algebra work. This idea will be revisited in other problems, as well as in other units. We do not expect students to develop formal strategies for solving equations. Rather, we would like them to develop strategies that are sensible to them and incorporate what they are learning about adding and subtracting fractions.

Prior to doing Problem 2.2, you might consider having students share their whole-number subtraction strategies in a class opener so that you and the students can become familiar with the various whole-number subtraction strategies students are using.

Launch 2.2

You might start with a discussion of spices in general. Find out what spices students like, or which spices their parents use. The spice mixes given in the problem are often used in different ethnic recipes.

Lead into Problem 2.2 by setting the context of Reyna's spice shop. Talk with the students about how spices are sold (by weight). You might want to display Transparency 2.2, the recipe cards, while you read the problem with the students. It might also be helpful to bring a few spice containers of different weights to give students a sense of how much 2 or 3 ounces of spice is. Be sure students understand what is intended in Question D. When the class understands what is expected of them, give them a copy of Labsheet 2.2 and let them work on the questions. Use a Think-Pair-Share grouping arrangement.

Explore 2.2

As students work, look for different strategies to bring out in the summary. If students are having trouble getting started, remind them of the strategies they used in Problem 2.1. Sometimes students suggest that fractions be converted to decimals in order to solve problems. While this is not incorrect, the focus of this investigation is to develop strategies for working with fractions. Redirect students to find ways to work with fractions as fractions.

Suggested Questions

- *What denominator did you use in the Spice Parisienne recipe?* (10)

- *Why is this a good choice?* (You can change the 5ths to 10ths so all the denominators are the same.)

- *Could you have renamed the fractions as 20ths and solved the problem?* (Yes.)

- *Why?* (5 and 10 are factors of 20.)

Some students struggle when they have to change more than one fraction in order to find equivalent fractions. This is the case with the Garam Masala recipe in Question B.

INVESTIGATION 2

- *Is there a number of which 2, 3, and 4 are all factors? (12 or 24) How can you use that number as the denominator and rename all your fractions?*

When students have made sufficient progress, pull them together to discuss strategies and solutions. Depending upon your students, you might want to stop and discuss Questions A–C before having them work on Questions D and E. Students may need support as they transition from contextual to non-contextual situations. If students struggle with the use of variable notation in Question D, you might suggest they think of the variable N as a question mark.

Summarize 2.2

The focus of the summary is similar to that of the summary of Problem 2.1. The computations and the reasoning are equally important. Writing a number sentence does not prove that the sum or difference is correct. As students share their number sentences, help them pull together the mathematics of the problems and generalize their strategies. Use questions that focus on the role of equivalence as well as how they handled adding and subtracting mixed numbers.

Suggested Questions Have students display their answers for Questions A–C. Ask questions like the following:

- *Why did you change the denominators in the Spice Parisienne recipe to tenths? How did that help solve the problem?* (Having like denominators makes the fractions easy to add and subtract.)

- *Why did you choose 12 as the denominator in the Garam Masala recipe?* (It is a multiple of 2, 3, and 4.)

- *What tells you that a problem requires adding?* (A combining or putting-together situation.)

- *What are some strategies you have found useful when combining or adding quantities of spices?*

A strategy students might use is to combine quantities that go together easily before they rename fractions with common denominators. For example, when finding the total spice used in the

Garam Masala recipe, students may combine all the whole numbers, then the halves and fourths, followed by the thirds.

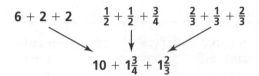

$$6 + 2 + 2 \qquad \tfrac{1}{2} + \tfrac{1}{2} + \tfrac{3}{4} \qquad \tfrac{2}{3} + \tfrac{1}{3} + \tfrac{2}{3}$$

$$10 + 1\tfrac{3}{4} + 1\tfrac{2}{3}$$

Now students take the problem $10 + 1\tfrac{3}{4} + 1\tfrac{2}{3}$ and find common denominators. When students combine quantities in this manner, be sure other students realize what they did and why.

Suggested Questions When students are comfortable with addition, shift the focus to subtraction.

- *What indicates that a problem will be a subtraction?* (taking away, how many more, or how much away situations)

Ask questions that direct students to share their actual computation strategies. For example:

- *How did you subtract the two amounts?*

Borrowing or renaming is needed to complete parts (2) and (3) in Question C. Help students to see that renaming is a way to create an equivalent fraction.

- *When a student tried to subtract $11\tfrac{1}{8} - 2\tfrac{5}{8}$ in Question C, part (2), he changed the 11 to a 10. Why?* (He needed to use the one he took from the 11 to make the extra eighths so he would have enough eighths to subtract.)

- *Why did he change the $\tfrac{1}{8}$ to $\tfrac{9}{8}$?* (Because the 1 he took from 11 is $\tfrac{8}{8}$, and $\tfrac{8}{8} + \tfrac{1}{8} = \tfrac{9}{8}$.)

- *Is $11\tfrac{1}{8}$ equivalent to $10\tfrac{9}{8}$?* (yes)

In one classroom, three strategies emerged for subtracting mixed numbers in situations when borrowing or regrouping is needed.

Some students drew upon their work with whole-number borrowing and used a borrowing algorithm.

Other students decided to rename the mixed numbers as improper fractions and then subtract. Borrowing is not needed when you do this.

A third group used a negative-number strategy that they also used when doing whole-number subtraction. While some students thought it was hard to understand at first, the students who used it were very proficient in using and explaining it. Here is an example of how this strategy works for the problem $4\frac{3}{8} - 2\frac{7}{8}$. Students start with either the whole numbers or the fractions and subtract to get $4 - 2 = 2$ and $\frac{3}{8} - \frac{7}{8} = -\frac{4}{8}$. Next students combine $-\frac{4}{8}$ and 2 as $2 - \frac{4}{8} = 1\frac{4}{8}$, or $1\frac{1}{2}$. If students don't normally use negatives when they subtract with whole numbers, they may be confused by this approach. You may need to spend a little time helping students understand.

Students are not expected to master all of these strategies. They should be able to use the strategies that they find sensible and efficient. What is important is that students try to understand the reasoning behind each strategy that is offered and decide whether it makes sense or not.

For Question D, have students share their approaches for finding N in each problem. In parts (1)–(4), N is a placeholder for the sum or difference. This is an opportunity to talk about the strategies that have emerged for finding sums and differences in non-contextual problems.

Parts (5) and (6) are missing-value problems. Ask students to share how they found their solutions. Students may rewrite the known values with common denominators, and then draw upon their whole-number knowledge to find the numerator of the unknown value. For example, in part (6), by rewriting $2\frac{2}{3} - N = 1\frac{1}{4}$ as $\frac{32}{12} - \frac{\blacksquare}{12} = \frac{15}{12}$, you can find the missing numerator value by solving $32 - \blacksquare = 15$, or $32 - N = 15$. Now you see that $N = \frac{17}{12}$, or $1\frac{5}{12}$.

Students may suggest the use of inverse operations as a solution strategy for finding N. If this does not come out here, that is fine. It is okay if students are struggling to make sense of missing-value problems. The strategy is more likely to emerge in the next problem when this type of problem will be revisited.

Use Question E to explicitly summarize strategies. We are not trying to write complete algorithms yet, but want to clarify the different approaches that have surfaced. This is a first attempt and it is okay if their reasoning is still fragile at this point. They will continue to articulate their reasoning as they work on the next two problems. The following represent some students' explanations.

> If you have quantities with different denominators, you can rename the fractions as equivalent fractions, add the parts, and then add the whole numbers. For example, in Question A, all of the fractions can be rewritten as 10ths. Some students might notice that the two one-tenths are equivalent to $\frac{1}{5}$ and then work the problem using 5ths. In Question B, the fractions can be rewritten as 12ths.

> Some students combine parts to make as many wholes as possible and then find ways to combine the remaining fractional parts. In Question B this is easy since $\frac{2}{3}$ and $\frac{1}{3}$ equals 1 whole and $2\frac{1}{2}$ and $6\frac{1}{2}$ is 9 wholes. This leaves students to make equivalent fractions using 12ths to add the remaining $\frac{2}{3}$ and $2\frac{3}{4}$.

> Some students rewrite mixed numbers as improper fractions when they have to subtract so they do not have to borrow. Some use negative numbers. Others rename one of their fractions so they can subtract the other.

If you assign Exercise 51 as homework for your students, you may want to point out the negative sign on the number line and explain what it means.

2.2 Visiting the Spice Shop: Using Addition and Subtraction

Mathematical Goals

- Write number sentences to represent situations for adding and subtracting fractions and mixed numbers
- Develop strategies for adding and subtracting fractions and mixed numbers

Launch

Introduce the problem context of spices and how various mixtures are used in recipes. Display Transparency 2.2 and talk about how Reyna's Spice Shop sells spices by weight. Read through the problem. Use a Think-Pair-Share grouping arrangement.

Materials
- Transparency 2.2

Explore

If students are having trouble getting started, remind them of the strategies they used in Problem 2.1. If students use decimal equivalents to add and subtract fractions, redirect them and let them know that while this is not wrong, the intention is to develop strategies for using fractions.

- *What denominator did you use in Question A?*
- *Why is this a good choice?*
- *Could you have renamed the fractions as 20ths?*

Some students struggle when they have to change more than one denominator. This is the case with Question B.

- *Is there a number of which 2, 3, and 4 are all factors? How can you use that number as the denominator and rename all your fractions?*

Materials
- Labsheet 2.2

Summarize

Focus on computation as well as reasoning. Have students display solutions.

- *Why did you change the denominators in Question A to 10ths? How did that help you solve the problem?*
- *What tells you that a problem requires adding?*
- *What are some useful strategies for adding quantities of spices?*
- *What indicates that a problem will be a subtraction?*
- *How did you subtract the two amounts?*
- *When a student tried to subtract $11\frac{1}{8} - 2\frac{5}{8}$ in Question C, part (2), he changed the 11 to a 10. Why? Why did he change the $\frac{1}{8}$ to $\frac{9}{8}$? Is $11\frac{1}{8}$ equivalent to $10\frac{9}{8}$?*

Materials
- Student notebooks

continued on next page

Summarize

continued

When multiple strategies surface, for example with borrowing, make it clear that students do not have to use all the strategies. They should try to make sense of all the strategies, but they need to be proficient with only one.

Questions D and E are used as a transition from contextualized problems to non-contextualized situations. In Question D, parts (5) and (6) focus on students' strategies for finding the value of the unknown. Do not push students to develop or use formal procedures or notation. Use Question E to summarize strategies. We are not trying to write complete algorithms yet. It is okay if their reasoning is still fragile.

ACE Assignment Guide for Problem 2.2

Differentiated Instruction
Solutions for All Learners

Core 4, 6–12, 30–35
Other *Applications* 3, 5, 13; *Connections* 36–38; *Extensions* 48, 51; unassigned choices from previous problems

Adapted For suggestions about adapting Exercises 5, 6, and other ACE exercises, see the CMP *Special Needs Handbook.*
Connecting to Prior Units 30–38: *Bits and Pieces I*

Answers to Problem 2.2

A. 1. $3\frac{9}{10}$ oz

   2. a. $2\frac{7}{10}$ oz; One strategy might be to add the fractions again, leaving out the nutmeg. Another might be to subtract $1\frac{1}{5}$ from the sum in part (1).

   b. $3\frac{9}{10} - 1\frac{1}{5} = 2\frac{7}{10}$ oz

B. 1. $13\frac{5}{12}$ oz

   2. a. $12\frac{1}{12}$ oz

   b. $13\frac{5}{12} - 1\frac{1}{3} = 12\frac{1}{12}$ oz

C. 1. $11\frac{1}{8}$ oz

   2. $8\frac{1}{2}$ oz

   3. $6\frac{7}{8}$ oz

D. 1. $N = 4\frac{4}{9}$

   2. $N = \frac{13}{20}$

   3. $N = 1\frac{5}{12}$

   4. $N = 1\frac{5}{12}$

   5. $N = \frac{3}{4}$

   6. $N = 1\frac{5}{12}$

E. A possible strategy for adding mixed numbers: First, see if you need to rewrite the fractions so they have the same denominator. Next, add the whole numbers and then add the fractions. When you add the fractions, add the numerators and put the sum over the denominator. If the sum of your fractions is an improper fraction, you should rename the improper fraction as a whole number and a fraction. Finally, combine the whole number from your improper fraction with the whole numbers from the original problem.

A possible strategy for subtracting mixed numbers: First, you need to rewrite the fractions so they have the same denominator. Next, decide if you can subtract the fractions. If you can, subtract the fractions and then subtract the whole numbers. If you need to borrow so you can subtract the fractions, take one of the wholes and rename it as a fraction. Combine it with the fraction from which you are subtracting. Finally, subtract the whole numbers and the fractions.

Just the Facts

Goals

- Explore the inverse relationship between the addition and subtraction of fractions

- Develop and use efficient strategies for adding and subtracting fractions and mixed numbers

Your students may have had exposure to inverse operations or "fact families" in elementary school. This idea is a powerful way to show that addition and subtraction are related and later that multiplication and division are related. Again, a variable is used as a placeholder. Allow students to use approaches that make sense to them. We are not trying to develop formal strategies for solving such problems and they should not be the focus of the conversation. We hope that some students will use inverse relationships to solve these problems so a conversation about this strategy can take place and set the stage for later work in algebra units.

Mathematics Background

For background on inverse relationships, see page 12.

Launch 2.3

Use the introduction to the problem to structure a conversation. Begin with whole numbers then fractions to help students attach what they are learning to what they already know. Do additional examples as needed for your students.

When you feel your students understand what a fact family is, read through the problem together. Have students work in small groups.

Explore 2.3

Look for students who have clever ways of thinking about fact families for your class summary.

Question A provides complete number sentences. Students will have to do some computation for the remaining questions. Ask

students to justify why their work makes sense to them. Continue to stress that writing a number sentence is not necessarily proof that the sum or difference is correct.

Suggested Questions

- *How do you know your number sentence is accurate?*

Note the strategies that students use to solve Question B. If they are not apparent, ask a question like the following:

- *Can you tell me how you figured out what the missing number was in the problem?*

Students may struggle with the use of two variables in Question D. Point out that M and N are different letters and represent different numbers that can be used together to make the number sentence total 3. It might be helpful for some students to see the problem rewritten in the following way: $\frac{5}{8} + \frac{1}{4} + \frac{2}{3} + \blacksquare + \blacksquare = 3$.

Summarize 2.3

The summary is an opportunity for students to articulate their addition and subtraction strategies. Have students share the fact families they developed in Question A. Ask students to explain how they thought about the problem.

Suggested Questions For Question B, parts (1) and (2), focus on how students added or subtracted to find the missing sum or difference.

- *What strategy did you use when adding? What strategy did you use when subtracting?*

- *Can your strategy be used on any addition problem? On any subtraction problem?* (Students do not have to have formal fraction addition or subtraction algorithms at this point. This question is meant to get students to think about whether or not a strategy can work in more than one situation.)

Question B, parts (3) and (4), have missing values. Ask questions that focus students on more than the answers found. Look for a place to introduce the use of inverse operations as a strategy for finding missing values. Question C will help you do this, but the strategy may also come out when working on Question B. If so, help students use fact families to make sense of why you might want to subtract to find the missing value in a problem like $\frac{3}{4} + N = \frac{17}{12}$.

- *How did you find the missing value in Question B, part (3)?* (I subtracted $\frac{3}{4}$ from $\frac{17}{12}$.)

- *Why does that seem reasonable?* (You can use subtraction to find the missing value in an addition problem. With a problem like $2 + \blacksquare = 5$, or $2 + N = 5$, you can subtract 2 from 5 to find the missing number.)

- *How does the fact family help us think about solving $\frac{3}{4} + N = \frac{17}{12}$?* (We can take the sum and subtract one of the addends to get the other addend.)

- *Did anyone use a different approach in part (3)?* (I renamed $\frac{3}{4}$ as $\frac{9}{12}$ and then I could see that if I added $\frac{8}{12}$ to $\frac{9}{12}$ I would have $\frac{17}{12}$.)

Lead the discussion to Question C. Have students share whether they agree or disagree with Rochelle's claim.

With Question D, look for opportunities to connect Rochelle's claim to students' reasoning. If students add up the three known quantities and then subtract this sum from 3, they are using subtraction to help them solve, or undo, an addition situation. For example,

$\frac{5}{8} + \frac{1}{4} + \frac{2}{3} + M + N = 3$ is equivalent to

$1\frac{13}{24} + M + N = 3$.

From here, you subtract $1\frac{13}{24}$ from 3 to get $1\frac{11}{24}$, the missing value that makes the sum 3. You can then use this value to find two fractions to use for M and N that total $1\frac{11}{24}$.

2.3 Just the Facts

Mathematical Goals

- Explore the inverse relationship between the addition and subtraction of fractions
- Develop and use efficient strategies for adding and subtracting fractions and mixed numbers

Launch

Use the introduction to the problem to structure a conversation. Do additional examples as needed for your students. When students understand what a fact family is, read through the problem together. Have students work in small groups.

Vocabulary
- fact family

Explore

Question A provides complete number sentences. Students will have to do computation for the remaining questions. Note the strategies students use to solve Question B. If they are not apparent, ask:

- *Can you tell me how you figured out what the missing number was in the problem?*

Students may struggle with the use of two variables in Question D. Point out that M and N are different letters representing different numbers that can be used together to make the number sentence total 3. For some students, rewriting the problem with questions marks in place of M and N may be helpful.

Summarize

Use the summary as an opportunity to articulate addition and subtraction strategies. Ask students to explain how they thought about the problem. For problems with missing values, ask questions to focus on more than answers. Focus on strategies and justification.

- *What strategy did you use when adding? When subtracting?*
- *Is your strategy one that can be used on any addition problem? On any subtraction problem?*
- *How did you find the missing value in Question B, part (3)? Why does that seem reasonable?*
- *How does the fact family help us think about solving $\frac{3}{4} + N = \frac{17}{12}$?*
- *Did anyone use a different approach?*

Materials
- Student notebooks

continued on next page

Wrap up the summary by discussing Rochelle's claim in Question C. With Question D, and previously, look for opportunities to connect Rochelle's claim to students' reasoning. If students add up the three known quantities and then subtract this sum from 3, they are using subtraction to help them solve, or undo, an addition situation.

Materials
- Student notebooks

ACE Assignment Guide for Problem 2.3

Core 14–18, 41–44
Other *Connections* 39, 40; *Extensions* 49; unassigned choices from previous problems

Adapted For suggestions about adapting Exercise 14 and other ACE exercises, see the CMP *Special Needs Handbook*.
Connecting to Prior Units 39–44: *Bits and Pieces I*

Answers to Problem 2.3

A. 1. $\frac{2}{3} + \frac{5}{9} = \frac{11}{9}, \frac{5}{9} + \frac{2}{3} = \frac{11}{9}, \frac{11}{9} - \frac{2}{3} = \frac{5}{9}$, and $\frac{11}{9} - \frac{5}{9} = \frac{2}{3}$.

2. $\frac{5}{10} - \frac{2}{5} = \frac{1}{10}, \frac{5}{10} - \frac{1}{10} = \frac{2}{5}, \frac{2}{5} + \frac{1}{10} = \frac{5}{10}$, and $\frac{1}{10} + \frac{2}{5} = \frac{5}{10}$.

B. 1. $N = 5\frac{4}{15}$; fact family: $3\frac{3}{5} + 1\frac{2}{3} = 5\frac{4}{15}$, $1\frac{2}{3} + 3\frac{3}{5} = 5\frac{4}{15}, 5\frac{4}{15} - 1\frac{2}{3} = 3\frac{3}{5}$, and $5\frac{4}{15} - 3\frac{3}{5} = 1\frac{2}{3}$.

2. $N = 1\frac{1}{2}$; fact family: $3\frac{1}{6} - 1\frac{2}{3} = 1\frac{1}{2}$, $3\frac{1}{6} - 1\frac{1}{2} = 1\frac{2}{3}, 1\frac{1}{2} + 1\frac{2}{3} = 3\frac{1}{6}$, and $1\frac{2}{3} + 1\frac{1}{2} = 3\frac{1}{6}$.

3. $N = \frac{2}{3}$; fact family: $\frac{3}{4} + \frac{2}{3} = \frac{17}{12}, \frac{2}{3} + \frac{3}{4} = \frac{17}{12}$, $\frac{17}{12} - \frac{3}{4} = \frac{2}{3}$, and $\frac{17}{12} - \frac{2}{3} = \frac{3}{4}$.

4. $N = \frac{7}{8}$; fact family: $\frac{7}{8} - \frac{1}{2} = \frac{3}{8}, \frac{7}{8} - \frac{3}{8} = \frac{1}{2}$, $\frac{3}{8} + \frac{1}{2} = \frac{7}{8}$, and $\frac{1}{2} + \frac{3}{8} = \frac{7}{8}$.

C. Agree. Possible explanation: If you know that $\frac{2}{3} + \frac{5}{9} = \frac{11}{9}$, you can use this information to find the solution to $\frac{11}{9} - \frac{2}{3}$. If you subtract one addend in the addition problem from the sum of the addition problem, the difference will be the other addend. This is a way to find the solution to the problem $\frac{2}{3} + N = \frac{11}{9}$.

D. Possible answers: $\frac{5}{8} + \frac{1}{4} + \frac{2}{3} + \frac{1}{8} + 1\frac{1}{3} = 3$; $\frac{5}{8} + \frac{1}{4} + \frac{2}{3} + \frac{11}{24} + 1 = 3$.

Designing Algorithms for Addition and Subtraction

Goal

- Develop an efficient algorithm for adding and subtracting fractions

In Question A students are given three groups of addition problems. The problems in each group have something in common. Each group brings out a special case of addition.

Group 1: fractions with common denominators

Group 2: cases where one denominator is a factor of the other and only one fraction needs to be renamed to make fractions with common denominators

Group 3: cases where both fractions have to be renamed to make fractions with common denominators

By making these subtle aspects of fraction addition explicit, we hope students will be able to write a general algorithm for adding any two fractions or mixed numbers. Addition problems that require regrouping or carrying can occur in any of these three categories. Each category has a problem where this occurs.

Question B is similar to Question A but focuses on subtraction. There are no problems where borrowing is needed. Borrowing can happen in each of the three cases, but it is addressed separately in parts (5) and (6).

Question C provides additional practice using the algorithms students have developed with carefully chosen problems. The problems may take more than one class period. Some teachers assign Question C as homework and discuss it on the following day.

Launch 2.4

Read the introduction to Problem 2.4 in the Student Edition. Talk with your class about what an algorithm is in mathematics.

Suggested Question

- *Can someone describe the algorithm you use for changing fractions to decimals or decimals to fractions?*

Record what students say and revise the written algorithm until the class agrees that what is written makes sense. This will help students to understand what is necessary for a complete description.

When the students understand what an algorithm is, have them begin work on the problem. Have students work individually on parts (1)–(3) of Questions A and B. Once they have found solutions, have students work in pairs or small groups to discuss their solutions and write algorithms.

Explore 2.4

Make sure students check their solutions and discuss the groups before moving on to the algorithms.

Have groups put their final addition and subtraction algorithms on large sheets of paper or transparencies. These can be shared with the class during the summary.

Summarize 2.4

Some teachers summarize Questions A and B together. Others summarize Question A, have students work on Question B, and then summarize Question B.

Suggested Questions Ask questions like the following:

- *Can someone describe what the problems in Group 1 have in common? In Group 2? In Group 3?*

- *Would someone share their addition (or subtraction) algorithm?*

- *What do others think about this group's algorithm? Will it work for all addition (or subtraction) cases?*

- *How does this algorithm compare to yours?*

- *Why is it important to have fractions with the same denominators?*

Evaluating whether each algorithm is usable and comparing it with other algorithms will further students' understanding of adding and subtracting fractions. As each algorithm is presented, students may not be able to completely understand the algorithm unless they try to use it. As students describe their algorithms, encourage them to use their example problems from part (3) of Questions A and B to show how their algorithm works. When it seems appropriate, have the class test a group's algorithm as a way to evaluate whether it is useable and helpful.

- *Let's try this algorithm on this problem. (Give an appropriate problem.) Does it work? Does it account for all the things that you have to think about to solve this problem?*

The class does not have to develop one agreed-upon algorithm, but students should have at least one algorithm for addition and one for subtraction that they can explain and use.

The problems in Question C were purposefully chosen. The first two problems use the same quantities but the placement of the whole numbers and mixed numbers determines how to proceed. Part (1) presents a situation where borrowing is needed but students may not realize this is the case. Part (2) is similar to part (1), but borrowing is not required in this situation. Part (3) uses a common denominator that is larger than ones encountered before and does not draw upon basic multiplication facts. Part (4) has three addends. Students have to regroup or carry after they add, but rather than add 1 as they have in most of the problems, a 2 is carried in this problem.

After the class discussion, you might ask students to take their algorithms home to show their families to see whether they can understand what the student has written and why the strategy makes sense.

2.4 Designing Algorithms for Addition and Subtraction

Mathematical Goal

- Develop an efficient algorithm for adding and subtracting fractions

Launch

Talk about what an algorithm is in mathematics.

- *Can someone describe the algorithm they use for changing fractions to decimals or decimals to fractions.*

Record what students are saying and revise the written algorithm until the class agrees that what is written makes sense. This will help students understand what is necessary for a complete description.

Once students understand what an algorithm is, have them begin individually on parts (1)–(3) of Questions A and B. Once students have found solutions, have them work in pairs or small groups to discuss their solutions and write algorithms.

Materials
- Transparencies 2.4A and 2.4B

Vocabulary
- algorithm

Explore

Make sure students check their solutions and discuss the groups before moving on to the algorithms.

Have groups put their final addition and subtraction algorithms on large sheets of paper or blank transparencies to share in summary.

Materials
- Large sheets of chart paper or blank transparency film
- Markers

Summarize

Some teachers summarize Questions A and B together. Others summarize Question A, have students work on Question B, and then summarize Question B.

- *Can someone describe what the problems in Group 1 have in common? In Group 2? In Group 3?*
- *Would someone share their addition (or subtraction) algorithm?*
- *Why is it important to have fractions with the same denominators?*
- *Will this algorithm work for all cases of addition (or subtraction)?*
- *Did anyone develop a different addition (or subtraction) algorithm?*

As each algorithm is presented, students may not completely understand it unless they try to use it. As students describe their algorithms, encourage students to use their example problems from part (3) of Questions A and B to show how their algorithm works. When appropriate, have the class test a group's algorithm as a way to evaluate whether it is useable and helpful.

- *Let's try this algorithm on this problem. (Give an appropriate problem.) Does it work? Does it account for all the things you have to think about to solve this problem?*

Materials
- Student notebooks

continued on next page

The class does not have to develop one agreed-upon algorithm but students should have at least one algorithm for addition and one for subtraction.

ACE Assignment Guide for Problem 2.4

Differentiated Instruction
Solutions for All Learners

Core 19–25, 46, 47
Other *Applications* 26, 27; *Connections* 45; *Extensions* 50; unassigned choices from previous problems

Adapted For suggestions about adapting ACE exercises, see the CMP *Special Needs Handbook*.
Connecting to Prior Units 46, 47: *Bits and Pieces I*

Answers to Problem 2.4

A. 1.

Group 1	Group 2	Group 3
$2\frac{6}{9}$ or $2\frac{2}{3}$	$\frac{7}{9}$	$\frac{19}{24}$
$\frac{6}{8}$ or $\frac{3}{4}$	$2\frac{11}{12}$	$3\frac{17}{36}$
$\frac{12}{5}$ or $2\frac{2}{5}$	$\frac{11}{8}$ or $1\frac{3}{8}$	$7\frac{11}{20}$

2. Group 1: fractions with common denominators

Group 2: cases where the denominator of one fraction is a factor of the denominator of the other and only one fraction needs to be renamed to make fractions with common denominators

Group 3: cases where both fractions have to be renamed to make fractions with common denominators

3. Answers will vary.

4. Answers will vary. Look for big ideas such as the need to rename the fractions so they have the same denominator. With adding, students might talk about needing to add the whole numbers and then add the fractions (or reverse). They may also talk about the need to rename a quantity when the whole number and fraction quantities are combined. For example, you might need to rewrite a solution like $4\frac{6}{5}$ as $5\frac{1}{5}$.

B. 1.

Group 1	Group 2	Group 3
$3\frac{4}{6}$ or $3\frac{2}{3}$	$1\frac{5}{8}$	$2\frac{7}{12}$
$\frac{10}{7}$ or $1\frac{3}{7}$	$\frac{3}{16}$	$\frac{1}{20}$
$1\frac{1}{3}$	$3\frac{1}{8}$	$4\frac{4}{15}$

2. Group 1: fractions with common denominators

Group 2: cases where the denominator of one fraction is a factor of the denominator of the other and only one fraction needs to be renamed to make fractions with common denominators

Group 3: cases where both fractions have to be renamed to make fractions with common denominators

3. Answers will vary.

4. Answers will vary. This algorithm should include the need for renaming fractions so they have common denominators.

5.

Group 1	Group 2	Group 3
$\frac{2}{3}$	$2\frac{7}{8}$	$1\frac{5}{12}$

Possible explanation: These problems are different from the problems above because each of these problems requires borrowing or renaming of the first fraction so the second fraction can be subtracted from it.

6. Answers will vary. Their algorithms should include an efficient strategy for dealing with subtraction situations where borrowing is needed. See the introduction to Investigation 2 for a discussion of three possible strategies upon which students may draw.

C. 1. $5\frac{1}{3}$ **2.** $6\frac{2}{3}$ **3.** $2\frac{127}{144}$ **4.** $5\frac{23}{60}$

The student edition pages for this
investigation begin on the next page.

Notes _____

_____

_____

Adding and Subtracting Fractions

Knowing how to combine and separate quantities is helpful in understanding the world around you. The mathematical names for combining and separating quantities are *adding* and *subtracting*.

For example, if you own two acres of land and you buy another half-acre lot, you will have $2 + \frac{1}{2}$, or $2\frac{1}{2}$, acres of land. The number sentence that shows this relationship is:

$$2 + \frac{1}{2} = 2\frac{1}{2}$$

The *sum* refers to the $2\frac{1}{2}$ acres of land you own.

If you then sell $\frac{3}{4}$ of an acre of your land, you will own $2\frac{1}{2} - \frac{3}{4}$ acres of land. The number sentence that shows this relationship is:

$$2\frac{1}{2} - \frac{3}{4} = 1\frac{3}{4}$$

The *difference* refers to the $1\frac{3}{4}$ acres of land you will own.

The problems in this investigation require you to add and subtract fractions. As you work, use what you have learned in earlier units and investigations about fractions and finding equivalent fractions. Practice writing number sentences to communicate your strategies for solving the problem.

Notes _____

_____

_____

_____

2.1 Land Sections

When Tupelo Township was founded, the land was divided into sections that could be farmed. Each *section* is a square that is 1 mile long on each side. In other words, each section is 1 square mile of land. There are 640 acres of land in a square-mile section.

Notes _____

_____

_____

_____

The diagram below shows two sections of land that are *adjacent*, or side by side. Each section is divided among several owners. The diagram shows the part of a section each person owns.

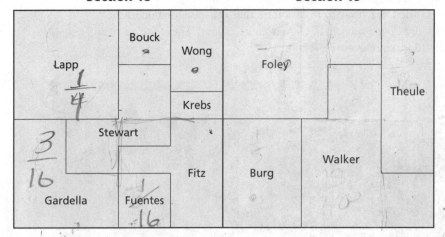

Section 18   Section 19

Problem **2.1** **Writing Addition and Subtraction Sentences**

A. What fraction of a section does each person own? Explain.

B. Suppose Fuentes buys Theule's land. What fraction of a section will Fuentes own? Write a number sentence to show your solution.

C. 1. Find a group of owners whose combined land is equal to $1\frac{1}{2}$ sections of land. Write a number sentence to show your solution.

2. Find another group of owners whose combined land is equal to $1\frac{1}{2}$ sections of land.

D. 1. Bouck and Lapp claim that when their land is combined, the total equals Foley's land. Write a number sentence to show whether this is true.

2. Find two other people whose combined land equals another person's land. Write a number sentence to show your answer.

3. Find three people whose combined land equals another person's land. Write a number sentence to show your answer.

E. How many acres of land does each person own? Explain your reasoning.

18 Bits and Pieces II

Notes

F. Lapp and Wong went on a land-buying spree and together bought all the lots of Section 18 that they did not already own. First, Lapp bought the land from Gardella, Fuentes, and Fitz. Then Wong bought the rest.

   1. When the buying was completed, what fraction of Section 18 did Lapp own?

   2. What fraction of Section 18 did Wong own?

   3. Who owned more land? How much more land did he or she own?

 ACE Homework starts on page 24.

2.2 Visiting the Spice Shop

All over the world cooks use spices to add flavor to foods. Because recipe ingredients are often measured using fractions, cooking can involve adding and subtracting fractional quantities.

Notes _____

_____

_____

_____

Reyna owns a spice shop in Tupelo Township. Some of her recipes are shown below.

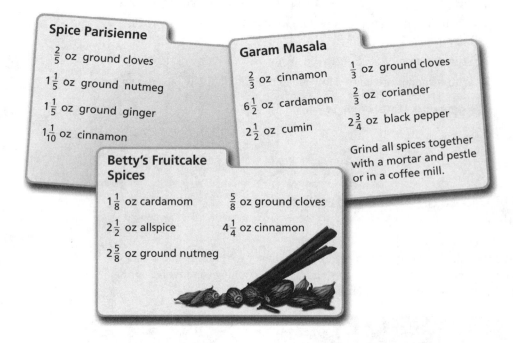

Spice Parisienne

$\frac{2}{5}$ oz ground cloves

$1\frac{1}{5}$ oz ground nutmeg

$1\frac{1}{5}$ oz ground ginger

$1\frac{1}{10}$ oz cinnamon

Garam Masala

$\frac{2}{3}$ oz cinnamon $\frac{1}{3}$ oz ground cloves

$6\frac{1}{2}$ oz cardamom $\frac{2}{3}$ oz coriander

$2\frac{1}{2}$ oz cumin $2\frac{3}{4}$ oz black pepper

Grind all spices together with a mortar and pestle or in a coffee mill.

Betty's Fruitcake Spices

$1\frac{1}{8}$ oz cardamom $\frac{5}{8}$ oz ground cloves

$2\frac{1}{2}$ oz allspice $4\frac{1}{4}$ oz cinnamon

$2\frac{5}{8}$ oz ground nutmeg

Problem 2.2 Using Addition and Subtraction

Use number sentences to show your thinking.

A. Latisha buys the spices to make one batch of Spice Parisienne.

   1. How many ounces of spice does Latisha buy?

   2. a. Suppose she already has the nutmeg at home. How many ounces of spice does she buy?

      b. Show a way to determine the answer using subtraction.

B. Ms. Garza buys spices to make one batch of Garam Masala.

   1. How many ounces of spice does Ms. Garza buy?

   2. a. Suppose she already has enough cinnamon and coriander at home. How many ounces of spice does she buy?

      b. Show a way to determine the answer using subtraction.

C. Betty buys spices for her famous fruitcake.

   1. How many ounces of spice does Betty buy?

   2. Betty makes the fruitcake but forgets the nutmeg! How many ounces of spice does she actually use?

Notes _____

_____

_____

_____

3. Tevin is allergic to cinnamon. If Betty removes cinnamon from the recipe for him, how many ounces of spice does she buy?

D. Use what you have learned to find the value for N that makes each sentence correct.

1. $1\frac{2}{3} + 2\frac{7}{9} = N$

2. $\frac{2}{5} + \frac{1}{4} = N$

3. $2\frac{3}{4} - 1\frac{1}{3} = N$

4. $3\frac{1}{6} - 1\frac{3}{4} = N$

5. $N + \frac{3}{4} = 1\frac{1}{2}$

6. $2\frac{2}{3} - N = 1\frac{1}{4}$

E. Describe a good strategy for adding and subtracting mixed numbers.

ACE Homework starts on page 24.

2.3 Just the Facts

$\mathbf{I}$n Problem 2.2, you wrote an addition or subtraction sentence to show a calculation you did. For each addition sentence you write, there are three related number sentences that show the same information.

$$\text{addition sentence:} \quad 2 + 3 = 5$$
$$\text{related number sentences:} \quad 3 + 2 = 5$$
$$5 - 2 = 3$$
$$5 - 3 = 2$$

These four number sentences form a **fact family.**

You can also create fact families with fractions. For example, $\frac{3}{4} + \frac{1}{8} = \frac{7}{8}$ has these three related number sentences:

$$\frac{1}{8} + \frac{3}{4} = \frac{7}{8}$$
$$\frac{7}{8} - \frac{3}{4} = \frac{1}{8}$$
$$\frac{7}{8} - \frac{1}{8} = \frac{3}{4}$$

You can write this entire fact family using eighths by changing $\frac{3}{4}$ to $\frac{6}{8}$. It looks like this:

$$\frac{6}{8} + \frac{1}{8} = \frac{7}{8}$$
$$\frac{1}{8} + \frac{6}{8} = \frac{7}{8}$$
$$\frac{7}{8} - \frac{6}{8} = \frac{1}{8}$$
$$\frac{7}{8} - \frac{1}{8} = \frac{6}{8}$$

Investigation 2 Adding and Subtracting Fractions   **21**

Notes _____

_____

_____

_____

Problem 2.3 Fact Families

A. For each number sentence, write its complete fact family.

1. $\frac{2}{3} + \frac{5}{9} = \frac{11}{9}$
2. $\frac{5}{10} - \frac{2}{5} = \frac{1}{10}$

B. For each mathematical sentence, find the value of N. Then write each complete fact family.

1. $3\frac{3}{5} + 1\frac{2}{3} = N$
2. $3\frac{1}{6} - 1\frac{2}{3} = N$

3. $\frac{3}{4} + N = \frac{17}{12}$
4. $N - \frac{1}{2} = \frac{3}{8}$

C. After writing several fact families, Rochelle claims that subtraction undoes addition. Do you agree or disagree? Explain your reasoning.

D. In the mathematical sentence below, find values for M and N that make the sum exactly 3. Write your answer as a sum that equals 3.

$$\frac{5}{8} + \frac{1}{4} + \frac{2}{3} + M + N = 3$$

ACE Homework starts on page 24.

2.4 Designing Algorithms for Addition and Subtraction

To become skilled in solving problems that involve addition and subtraction of fractions, you need a plan for carrying out computations. In mathematics, a plan, or a series of steps, for doing a computation is called an **algorithm** (AL guh rith um). For an algorithm to be useful, each step should be clear and precise.

In this problem, you develop algorithms for adding and subtracting fractions. You may develop more than one for each computation. You should understand and feel comfortable with at least one algorithm for adding fractions and at least one algorithm for subtracting fractions.

22 Bits and Pieces II

Notes _____

_____

_____

_____

A. 1. Find the sums in each group.

Group 1	Group 2	Group 3
$2\frac{2}{9} + \frac{4}{9}$	$\frac{4}{9} + \frac{1}{3}$	$\frac{1}{8} + \frac{2}{3}$
$\frac{5}{8} + \frac{1}{8}$	$2\frac{1}{2} + \frac{5}{12}$	$\frac{2}{9} + 3\frac{1}{4}$
$\frac{3}{5} + \frac{9}{5}$	$\frac{7}{8} + \frac{1}{2}$	$3\frac{4}{5} + 3\frac{3}{4}$

2. Describe what the problems in each group have in common.

3. Make up one new problem that fits in each group.

4. Write an algorithm that will work for adding *any* two fractions including mixed numbers. Test your algorithm on the problems in the table. If necessary, change your algorithm until you think it will work all the time.

B. 1. Find the differences in each group.

Group 1	Group 2	Group 3
$3\frac{5}{6} - \frac{1}{6}$	$1\frac{3}{4} - \frac{1}{8}$	$3\frac{5}{6} - 1\frac{1}{4}$
$\frac{11}{7} - \frac{1}{7}$	$2\frac{7}{16} - 2\frac{1}{4}$	$\frac{1}{4} - \frac{1}{5}$
$1\frac{2}{3} - \frac{1}{3}$	$6\frac{7}{8} - 3\frac{3}{4}$	$4\frac{3}{5} - \frac{1}{3}$

2. Describe what the problems in each group have in common.

3. Make up one new problem that fits in each group.

4. Write an algorithm that will work for subtracting *any* two fractions, including mixed numbers. Test your algorithm on the problems in the table.

5. Describe how the subtraction problems below are different from the problems in the subtraction table in part (1).

Group 1	Group 2	Group 3
$1\frac{1}{3} - \frac{2}{3}$	$6\frac{3}{4} - 3\frac{7}{8}$	$3\frac{1}{4} - 1\frac{5}{6}$

6. If needed, change your algorithm until you think it will work all the time.

C. Use your algorithms for addition and subtraction to find each sum or difference.

1. $8 - 2\frac{2}{3}$ **2.** $8\frac{2}{3} - 2$ **3.** $2\frac{7}{16} + \frac{4}{9}$ **4.** $1\frac{4}{5} + 1\frac{5}{6} + 1\frac{3}{4}$

ACE Homework starts on page 24.

Notes _____

_____

_____

Applications

1. The Langstons planted a big garden with flowers to sell to florists.

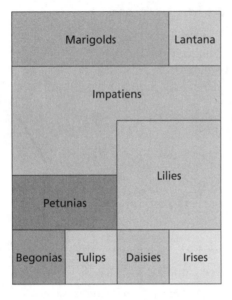

a. What fraction of the garden is planted with each type of flower?

b. How much more of the garden is planted with lilies than daisies?

c. Suppose the Langstons replace the daisies and irises with lilies. What fraction of the garden would be planted with lilies?

d. Use fractions to explain whether the following sentence is correct or incorrect.

The plots used for growing marigolds and petunias are equivalent to the plot used to grow impatiens.

e. Use fractions to explain whether the following sentence is correct or incorrect.

Marigolds − Begonias = Petunias + Tulips

f. Look at the original garden plan. Find three different combinations of plots that total the fraction of the garden planted with impatiens. Write a number sentence for each combination.

STUDENT PAGE

Notes _____

_____

_____

_____

2. A local magazine sells space for ads. It charges advertisers according to the fraction of a page each ad fills.

Sample Magazine Page

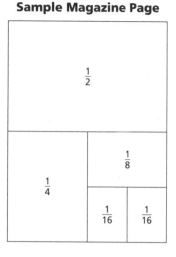

a. Advertisers purchase $\frac{1}{8}$ and $\frac{1}{16}$ of a page. What fraction of the page is used for ads?

b. What fraction of the page remains for other uses? Explain.

3. The Cool Sub Shop is having its grand opening. The owner buys three $\frac{1}{4}$-page ads, four $\frac{1}{8}$-page ads, and ten $\frac{1}{16}$-page ads. What is the total amount of ad space that the owner buys?

4. A local concert promoter purchases $2\frac{3}{4}$ pages of ads. When one of the concerts is cancelled, the promoter cancels $1\frac{5}{8}$ pages of ads. How much advertising space is the concert promoter actually using?

5. Rico and his friend eat part of a pan of lasagna. Rico eats $\frac{1}{16}$ of the lasagna, and his friend eats $\frac{1}{32}$ of the lasagna. How much of the lasagna is left?

6. Suppose you eat $\frac{3}{4}$ of a pizza and then eat $\frac{1}{8}$ of another pizza of the same size. How much of a whole pizza do you eat altogether?

For Exercises 7–12, find each sum or difference.

Go Online
PHSchool.com

7. $8\frac{11}{12} - 2\frac{3}{4}$

8. $4\frac{4}{9} + 1\frac{2}{9}$

9. $2\frac{1}{8} + 3\frac{3}{4} + 1\frac{1}{2}$

For: Multiple-Choice Skills Practice

10. $2\frac{7}{9} + 6\frac{1}{3}$

11. $11\frac{1}{2} - 2\frac{2}{3}$

12. $1\frac{2}{5} + 1\frac{1}{3}$

Web Code: ama-4254

13. Find each sum. Describe any patterns that you see.

a. $\frac{1}{2} + \frac{1}{3}$

b. $\frac{2}{4} + \frac{2}{6}$

c. $\frac{6}{12} + \frac{4}{12}$

For Exercises 14–17, determine which sum or difference is greater. Show your work.

14. $\frac{2}{3} + \frac{5}{6}$ or $\frac{3}{4} + \frac{4}{5}$

15. $\frac{7}{6} - \frac{2}{3}$ or $\frac{3}{5} - \frac{5}{10}$

16. $\frac{1}{4} + \frac{5}{6}$ or $\frac{1}{5} + \frac{7}{8}$

17. $\frac{1}{16} + \frac{1}{12}$ or $\frac{5}{4} - \frac{4}{5}$

Investigation 2 Adding and Subtracting Fractions   **25**

Notes _____

_____

_____

_____

18. Write the complete fact family for $\frac{1}{16} + \frac{1}{12}$ and for $\frac{5}{4} - \frac{4}{5}$.

19. Find the value for N that makes each number sentence correct.

a. $\frac{2}{3} + \frac{3}{4} = N$ **b.** $\frac{3}{4} + N = \frac{4}{5}$ **c.** $N - \frac{3}{5} = \frac{1}{4}$

For Exercises 20–25, find each sum or difference.

20. $2\frac{5}{6} + 1\frac{1}{3}$ **21.** $15\frac{5}{8} + 10\frac{5}{6}$ **22.** $4\frac{4}{9} + 2\frac{1}{5}$

23. $6\frac{1}{4} - 2\frac{5}{6}$ **24.** $3\frac{1}{2} - 1\frac{4}{5}$ **25.** $4\frac{1}{3} - \frac{5}{12}$

26. Find each sum. Describe any patterns that you see.

a. $\frac{1}{2} + \frac{1}{4}$ **b.** $\frac{1}{3} + \frac{1}{6}$ **c.** $\frac{1}{4} + \frac{1}{8}$

d. $\frac{1}{5} + \frac{1}{10}$ **e.** $\frac{1}{6} + \frac{1}{12}$ **f.** $\frac{1}{7} + \frac{1}{14}$

27. Tony works at a pizza shop. He cuts two pizzas into eight equal sections each. Customers then eat $\frac{7}{8}$ of each pizza. Tony says that $\frac{7}{8} + \frac{7}{8} = \frac{14}{16}$, so $\frac{14}{16}$ of all the pizza was eaten. Is Tony's addition correct? Explain.

Homework Help Online
PHSchool.com
For: Help with Exercise 27
Web Code: ame-4227

Connections

28. Suppose you select a number in the interval from $\frac{1}{2}$ to $\frac{3}{4}$ and a number in the interval from $\frac{3}{4}$ to $1\frac{1}{4}$. What is the least their sum can be? What is the greatest their sum can be? Explain your reasoning. (Note: The numbers $\frac{1}{2}$ and $\frac{3}{4}$ are included in the interval from $\frac{1}{2}$ to $\frac{3}{4}$.)

29. One number is near the benchmark $\frac{1}{4}$, and another is near the benchmark $1\frac{1}{2}$. Estimate their sum. Explain.

For Exercises 30–35, find a value for N that will make the sentence true.

30. $\frac{3}{12} = \frac{N}{8}$ **31.** $\frac{N}{4} = \frac{6}{8}$ **32.** $\frac{1}{2} = \frac{N}{12}$

33. $\frac{N}{12} = \frac{2}{3}$ **34.** $\frac{N}{8} = \frac{14}{16}$ **35.** $\frac{5}{12} = \frac{10}{N}$

Notes _____

_____

_____

_____

In Exercises 36–38, paint has spilled on the page, covering part of the fraction strips. Use what is showing to reason about each set of strips. Find the equivalent fractions indicated by the question marks.

36.

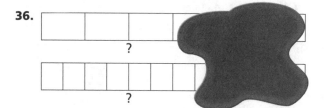

37.

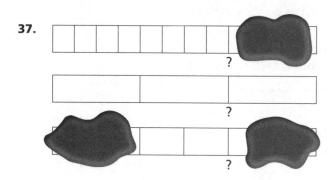

38.

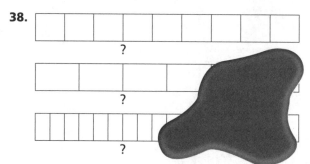

For Exercises 39 and 40, use the map of Tupelo Township from Problem 2.1.

39. Multiple Choice Choose the combination of landowners who together own exactly one hundred percent of a section.

A. Burg, Lapp, Wong, Fuentes, and Bouck

B. Burg, Lapp, Fuentes, Bouck, Wong, Theule, and Stewart

C. Lapp, Fitz, Foley, and Walker

D. Walker, Foley, Fitz, and Fuentes

40. Find two different combinations of landowners whose land is equal to 1.25 sections of land. Write number sentences to show your solutions.

Investigation 2 Adding and Subtracting Fractions   **27**

Notes

Copy each pair of numbers in Exercises 41–44. Insert <, >, or = to make a true statement.

41. 18.156 ■ 18.17

42. 3.184 ■ 31.84

43. 5.78329 ■ 5.78239

44. 4.0074 ■ 4.0008

45. When solving $\frac{7}{15} + \frac{2}{10}$, Maribel writes $\frac{70}{150} + \frac{30}{150}$.

  a. Show why $\frac{70}{150} + \frac{30}{150}$ is equivalent to $\frac{7}{15} + \frac{2}{10}$.

  b. Write two more addition problems that are equivalent to $\frac{7}{15} + \frac{2}{10}$.

  c. Of the three problems, Maribel's and the two you wrote, which one do you think will be the easiest to use to find the sum? Why?

46. The model at the right represents $\frac{1}{3}$ of a whole. Use the model to name the amounts shown in parts (a) and (b).

  a.

  b.

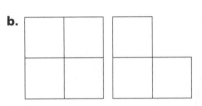

47. The following model represents one whole.

  a. Draw a picture to represent $1\frac{1}{3} + \frac{1}{6}$.

  b. Draw a picture to represent $2\frac{2}{3} - \frac{4}{3}$.

Notes _____

_____

_____

_____

Extensions

48. *The Spartan* magazine wants to charge $160 for each full page of advertising.

   a. Develop a pricing plan to show the cost for each size ad shown below. Explain.

   $\frac{1}{32}$ page, $\frac{1}{16}$ page, $\frac{1}{8}$ page, $\frac{1}{4}$ page, $\frac{1}{2}$ page, 1 page

   b. Use the pricing plan you developed. What is the bill for the Cool Sub Shop if the owner purchases three $\frac{1}{4}$-page ads, four $\frac{1}{8}$-page ads, and a $\frac{1}{16}$-page ad?

   c. The senior class is raising money for their senior trip. They have $80 to spend on advertising. Geraldo says they can purchase two $\frac{1}{8}$-page ads and four $\frac{1}{16}$-page ads with their money. According to your pricing plan in part (a), is he correct? Explain.

   d. Use your pricing plan from part (a). Find four different sets of ad sizes that the senior class can purchase for $80. Show why your answers are correct.

49. a. Find a number for each denominator to make the sentence true. If necessary, you may use a number more than once.

   $$\frac{1}{\blacksquare} - \frac{1}{\blacksquare} = \frac{1}{\blacksquare}$$

   b. Find another set of numbers that works.

50. It takes 8 people to clear an acre of weeds in 4 hours.

   a. How many acres can 16 people clear in 4 hours?

   b. How many acres can 2 people clear in 4 hours?

   c. How many people are needed to clear 3 acres in 4 hours?

   d. How many people are needed to clear 3 acres in 2 hours?

Notes _____

_____

_____

_____

51. The sixth-grade students at Cleveland Middle School are selling popcorn as a fundraiser. They keep track of their progress using a number line like the one below:

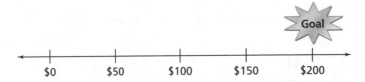

After Day 2, the students have not sold enough popcorn to make up for the money they spent getting started. Ms. Johnson suggests they change their number line to look like this:

a. The students then plot this point to show their progress:

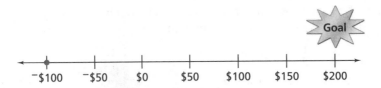

How much money have the sixth-graders lost?

b. After Day 4, the sixth-graders are doing better. They have lost a total of $25. Mark this point on a copy of the number line.

c. After Day 6, the sixth-graders are breaking even. This means they are no longer losing any money, but they are not gaining any money either. Mark their progress on your number line.

d. At the end of the fundraiser, the sixth-graders' number line looks like the one below. How much money have they raised?

e. What fraction of their goal did they raise after they broke even?

Notes _____

_____

_____

_____

Mathematical Reflections 2

In this investigation you explored ways to add and subtract fractions. These questions will help you to summarize what you have learned.

Think about your answers to these questions. Discuss your ideas with other students and your teacher. Then write a summary of your findings in your notebook.

1. Suppose you are helping a student who has not studied fractions. What is the most important thing you can say about adding or subtracting fractions?

2. Describe at least two things that you have to think about when you add or subtract with mixed numbers. Choose things that you do *not* need to think about when you add or subtract fractions.

3. Use an example to show how addition and subtraction of fractions are related in fact families.

STUDENT PAGE

Notes _____

_____

_____

_____

Investigation 2

ACE Assignment Choices

Differentiated Instruction
Solutions for All Learners

Problem 2.1
Core 2, 29
Other *Applications* 1, *Connections* 28

Problem 2.2
Core 4, 6–12, 30–35
Other *Applications* 3, 5, 13; *Connections* 36–38; *Extensions* 48, 51; unassigned choices from previous problems

Problem 2.3
Core 14–18, 41–44
Other *Connections* 39, 40; *Extensions* 49; unassigned choices from previous problems

Problem 2.4
Core 19–25, 46, 47
Other *Applications* 26, 27; *Connections* 45; *Extensions* 50; unassigned choices from previous problems

Adapted For suggestions about adapting Exercises 5, 6, 14, and other ACE exercises, see the CMP *Special Needs Handbook*.
Connecting to Prior Units 30–44, 46, 47: *Bits and Pieces I*

Applications

1. **a.** Marigolds: $\frac{3}{20}$; Lantana: $\frac{1}{20}$; Impatiens: $\frac{3}{10}$; Petunias: $\frac{1}{10}$; Lilies: $\frac{1}{5}$; Begonias: $\frac{1}{20}$; Tulips: $\frac{1}{20}$; Daisies: $\frac{1}{20}$; Irises: $\frac{1}{20}$

   b. $\frac{4}{20} - \frac{1}{20} = \frac{3}{20}$

   c. $\frac{4}{20} + \frac{1}{20} + \frac{1}{20} = \frac{6}{20}$ or $\frac{3}{10}$

d. Incorrect. Possible explanation: The fraction of land for marigolds and petunias $(\frac{3}{20} + \frac{2}{20})$ is $\frac{5}{20}$. The fraction of land for impatiens is $\frac{3}{10}$, or $\frac{6}{20}$ of the garden. The impatiens cover a larger amount of land.

e. Incorrect. Possible explanation: The number sentence for the situation is $\frac{3}{20} - \frac{1}{20} = \frac{1}{10} + \frac{1}{20}$. If you work out the subtraction problem on the left of the equal sign and the addition problem on the right, the answers are not the same.

f. Possible combinations that total $\frac{3}{10}$, the fraction planted with impatiens:

Marigolds + Petunias + Lantana:
$\frac{3}{20} + \frac{2}{20} + \frac{1}{20} = \frac{6}{20}$, or $\frac{3}{10}$

Lilies + Petunias: $\frac{4}{20} + \frac{2}{20} = \frac{6}{20}$, or $\frac{3}{10}$

Marigolds + Begonias + Tulips + Daisies:
$\frac{3}{20} + \frac{1}{20} + \frac{1}{20} + \frac{1}{20} = \frac{6}{20}$, or $\frac{3}{10}$

2. **a.** $\frac{1}{8} + \frac{1}{16} = \frac{3}{16}$ of the page is used for ads.

   b. $1 - \frac{3}{16} = \frac{13}{16}$ of the page remains.

3. $\frac{3}{4}$ (three $\frac{1}{4}$-page ads, or $3 \times \frac{1}{4}$) plus $\frac{4}{8}$ (four $\frac{1}{8}$-page ads, or $4 \times \frac{1}{8}$) plus $\frac{10}{16}$ (ten $\frac{1}{16}$-page ads, or $10 \times \frac{1}{16}$) $= 1\frac{7}{8}$ pages

4. $2\frac{3}{4} - 1\frac{5}{8} = 1\frac{1}{8}$ pages

5. $\frac{1}{16} + \frac{1}{32} = \frac{3}{32}$ of the lasagna is eaten, leaving $\frac{29}{32}$ of the lasagna uneaten.

6. $\frac{3}{4} + \frac{1}{8} = \frac{7}{8}$ of a pizza

7. $6\frac{2}{12}$ or $6\frac{1}{6}$ 8. $5\frac{6}{9}$ or $5\frac{2}{3}$

9. $7\frac{3}{8}$ 10. $9\frac{1}{9}$

11. $8\frac{5}{6}$

12. $2\frac{11}{15}$

13. a. $\frac{5}{6}$ **b.** $\frac{5}{6}$ **c.** $\frac{5}{6}$

Parts (b) and (c) are equivalent to part (a) $(\frac{1}{2} + \frac{1}{3})$.

14. $\frac{3}{4} + \frac{4}{5}$ is greater: $\frac{2}{3} + \frac{5}{6} = \frac{4}{6} + \frac{5}{6} = \frac{9}{6} = 1\frac{1}{2} = 1\frac{10}{20}$; $\frac{3}{4} + \frac{4}{5} = \frac{15}{20} + \frac{16}{20} = 1\frac{11}{20}$

15. $\frac{7}{6} - \frac{2}{3}$ is greater: $\frac{7}{6} - \frac{2}{3} = \frac{7}{6} - \frac{4}{6} = \frac{3}{6} = \frac{1}{2} = \frac{5}{10}$; $\frac{3}{5} - \frac{5}{10} = \frac{6}{10} - \frac{5}{10} = \frac{1}{10}$.

16. $\frac{1}{4} + \frac{5}{6}$ is greater: $\frac{1}{4} + \frac{5}{6} = \frac{3}{12} + \frac{10}{12} = 1\frac{1}{12} = 1\frac{10}{120}$; $\frac{1}{5} + \frac{7}{8} = \frac{8}{40} + \frac{35}{40} = 1\frac{3}{40} = 1\frac{9}{120}$.

17. $\frac{5}{4} - \frac{4}{5}$ is greater: $\frac{1}{16} + \frac{1}{12} = \frac{3}{48} + \frac{4}{48} = \frac{7}{48} = \frac{35}{240}$; $\frac{5}{4} - \frac{4}{5} = \frac{25}{20} - \frac{16}{20} = \frac{9}{20} = \frac{108}{240}$.

18. $\frac{1}{16} + \frac{1}{12} = \frac{7}{48}$, $\frac{1}{12} + \frac{1}{16} = \frac{7}{48}$, $\frac{7}{48} - \frac{1}{12} = \frac{1}{16}$, and $\frac{7}{48} - \frac{1}{16} = \frac{1}{12}$

$\frac{5}{4} - \frac{4}{5} = \frac{9}{20}$, $\frac{5}{4} - \frac{9}{20} = \frac{4}{5}$, $\frac{9}{20} + \frac{4}{5} = \frac{5}{4}$, and $\frac{4}{5} + \frac{9}{20} = \frac{5}{4}$

19. a. $N = 1\frac{5}{12}$

  b. $N = \frac{1}{20}$

  c. $N = \frac{17}{20}$

20. $2\frac{5}{6} + 1\frac{1}{3} = 4\frac{1}{6}$

21. $15\frac{5}{8} + 10\frac{5}{6} = 26\frac{11}{24}$

22. $4\frac{4}{9} + 2\frac{1}{5} = 6\frac{29}{45}$

23. $6\frac{1}{4} - 2\frac{5}{6} = 3\frac{5}{12}$

24. $3\frac{1}{2} - 1\frac{4}{5} = 1\frac{7}{10}$

25. $4\frac{1}{3} - \frac{5}{12} = 3\frac{11}{12}$

26. a. $\frac{3}{4}$ **b.** $\frac{3}{6}$ or $\frac{1}{2}$

  c. $\frac{3}{8}$ **d.** $\frac{3}{10}$

  e. $\frac{3}{12}$ **f.** $\frac{3}{14}$

In all of the problems, you add unit fractions where one fraction is half the size of the other. The fraction in each part with the lesser denominator is twice the value of the unit fraction with the greater denominator. You can think of the unit fraction with the lesser denominator as two unit fractions with the greater denominator. This gives a sum with a 3 in the numerator over the greater denominator.

27. No. If $\frac{14}{16}$ of all the pizza were eaten, this would be less than one whole pizza. If there are eight sections in each pizza, then people are eating eighths. And all together they ate $\frac{14}{8}$, or $1\frac{6}{8}$ pizzas.

Connections

28. Least sum: $\frac{1}{2} + \frac{3}{4} = 1\frac{1}{4}$. To get the least sum, you want to choose the least number in each interval. Greatest sum: $\frac{3}{4} + 1\frac{1}{4} = 2$. To get the greatest sum, you want to choose the greatest number in each interval.

29. $1\frac{3}{4}$. To find a sum using benchmarks, choose the nearest benchmark to each number, then add the benchmarks.

30. $\frac{3}{12} = \frac{2}{8}$ (N = 2)

31. $\frac{3}{4} = \frac{6}{8}$ (N = 3)

32. $\frac{1}{2} = \frac{6}{12}$ (N = 6)

33. $\frac{8}{12} = \frac{2}{3}$ (N = 8)

34. $\frac{7}{8} = \frac{14}{16}$ (N = 7)

35. $\frac{5}{12} = \frac{10}{24}$ (N = 24)

36. $\frac{2}{6} = \frac{4}{12}$

37. $\frac{8}{12} = \frac{2}{3} = \frac{4}{6}$

38. $\frac{3}{9} = \frac{2}{6} = \frac{6}{18}$

39. B

40. Possible answers: Everyone in Section 19 (Foley, Theule, Burg, and Walker) and Lapp from Section 18: $\frac{5}{16} + \frac{3}{16} + \frac{3}{16} + \frac{5}{16} + \frac{1}{4} = 1\frac{1}{4}$ or 1.25; Lapp, Bouck, Theule, Walker, Burg, Fitz, Fuentes, and Krebs: $\frac{1}{4} + \frac{1}{16} + \frac{3}{16} + \frac{5}{16} + \frac{3}{16} + \frac{5}{32} + \frac{1}{16} + \frac{1}{32} = 1\frac{1}{4}$ or 1.25).

41. $18.156 < 18.17$

42. $3.184 < 31.84$

43. $5.78329 > 5.78239$

44. $4.0074 > 4.0008$

45. a. If you multiply the numerator and denominator of $\frac{7}{15}$ by 10, you get the equivalent fraction $\frac{70}{150}$. If you multiply the numerator and denominator of $\frac{2}{10}$ by 15, you get $\frac{30}{150}$.

b. Possible answer: $\frac{14}{30} + \frac{6}{30}$ and $\frac{28}{60} + \frac{12}{60}$

c. Answers will vary based on part (b). Possible answer: $\frac{14}{30} + \frac{6}{30}$ uses the least common multiple of the two denominators, so it is the easiest to add.

46. a. $\frac{4}{3}$ or $1\frac{1}{3}$ **b.** $\frac{7}{9}$

47. a.

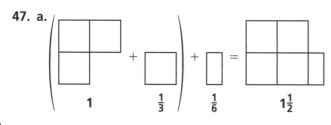

b. (Figure 2)

Extensions

48. a. The magazine could charge

$160 \div 32 = \$5$ for $\frac{1}{32}$ of a page,

$160 \div 16 = \$10$ for $\frac{1}{16}$ of a page,

$160 \div 8 = \$20$ for $\frac{1}{8}$ of a page,

$160 \div 4 = \$40$ for $\frac{1}{4}$ of a page,

$160 \div 2 = \$80$ for $\frac{1}{2}$ of a page, and

$160 for a whole page.

b. $(3 \times \$40) + (4 \times \$20) + \$10 = \$210$

c. Yes; $(2 \times \$20) + (4 \times \$10) = \$80$.

d. Possible answers:

two $\frac{1}{4}$-page ads $(2 \times \$40 = \$80)$;

four $\frac{1}{8}$-page ads $(4 \times \$20 = \$80)$;

eight $\frac{1}{16}$-page ads $(8 \times \$10 = \$80)$;

sixteen $\frac{1}{32}$-page ads $(16 \times \$5 = \$80)$;

one $\frac{1}{4}$-page ad and two $\frac{1}{8}$-page ads
$(1 \times \$40 + 2 \times \$20 = \$80)$;

two $\frac{1}{8}$-page ads and four $\frac{1}{16}$-page ads
$(2 \times \$20 + 4 \times \$10 = \$80)$

49. a–b. Possible answers: $\frac{1}{2} - \frac{1}{3} = \frac{1}{6}$; $\frac{1}{4} - \frac{1}{5} = \frac{1}{20}$

50. a. 2 acres   **b.** $\frac{1}{4}$ of an acre

c. 24 people   **d.** 48 people

51. a. The sixth-graders had lost $100.

b.

c.

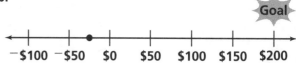

d. $175

e. $\frac{7}{8}$

Figure 2

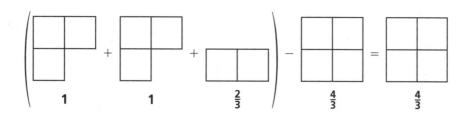

Possible Answers to Mathematical Reflections

1. Answers will vary. Look for big ideas such as the need to rename the fractions so they have the same denominator. With adding, students might talk about needing to add the whole numbers and then the fractions. They may also talk about the need to rename a quantity when the whole number and fraction quantities are combined. How students talk about subtracting fractions may vary depending on their preferred algorithm. For example, some students use a borrowing algorithm, some students use negative numbers, and other students use improper fractions.

2. When adding mixed numbers, you need to add the fractions and add the whole numbers. With subtraction, answers will vary depending on the algorithm that students are most comfortable with. For example, students who change mixed numbers to improper fractions will not talk about borrowing. Students who use a borrowing procedure should talk about the need to subtract the fractions and then the whole numbers.

3. Possible answer: $\frac{1}{2} + \frac{1}{3} = \frac{5}{6}, \frac{1}{3} + \frac{1}{2} = \frac{5}{6}, \frac{5}{6} - \frac{1}{2} = \frac{1}{3}$, and $\frac{5}{6} - \frac{1}{3} = \frac{1}{2}$.

Mathematical and Problem-Solving Goals

- Estimate products of fractions
- Use models to represent the product of two fractions
- Understand that finding a fraction *of* a number means multiplication
- Develop and use strategies and models for multiplying combinations of fractions, whole numbers, and mixed numbers to solve problems
- Determine when multiplication is an appropriate operation
- Explore the relationships between two numbers and their product
- Develop and use an efficient algorithm to solve any fraction multiplication problem

Summary of Problems

Problem 3.1 **How Much of a Pan Have We Sold?**

Students use square-area models for fraction multiplication.

Problem 3.2 **Finding a Part of a Part**

Students use thermometers and number lines as partitioning models.

Problem 3.3 **Modeling More Multiplication Situations**

Students extend their understanding of multiplication by modeling situations that involve fractions and mixed numbers.

Problem 3.4 **Changing Forms**

Students explore equivalent forms as a strategy to multiply fractions and mixed numbers.

Problem 3.5 **Writing a Multiplication Algorithm**

Students use multiplication problems grouped in categories to develop an efficient algorithm for fraction multiplication.

Mathematics Background

For background on fraction multiplication, see page 6.

	Suggested Pacing	Materials for Students	Materials for Teachers	ACE Assignments
All	$5\frac{1}{2}$ days	Calculators, blank transparencies and transparency markers, student notebooks	Blank transparencies and transparency markers	
3.1	1 day	Labsheet 3.1, colored pencils		1–5, 36, 37
3.2	1 day		Transparency 3.2	6–10, 38, 39
3.3	1 day		Transparency 3.3	11–15, 40–45, 48
3.4	1 day		Transparency 3.4	16–20, 46, 47, 49
3.5	1 day	Chart paper (optional)	Transparency 3.5	21–35
MR	$\frac{1}{2}$ day			

Goals

- Estimate products of fractions
- Use models to represent the product of two fractions
- Understand that finding a fraction *of* a number means multiplication

Students work with an area model for fractions in the context of brownie pans. In Questions A–C, allow students to find ways to make sense of the problem using the models. They do not need to develop a deep understanding of the algorithm at this stage. Instead, get them to think about what it means to find a "part of a part." Understanding that "part of a part" means "×" is raised in Question C. This helps students decide whether multiplication will help solve a problem in other situations. Question D is the first of many estimation problems in this investigation.

Launch 3.1

Explain that in this investigation they are going to work on another operation, multiplying fractions.

Suggested Questions Ask students:

- *Can you describe some situations where multiplication is used?*

After hearing a few examples, discuss the football-packing problem in the introduction to the investigation in the Student Edition to find out what students know about faction multiplication situations. Do students have any sense of how big or small the products are?

Then, use the Paulo and Shania problem to engage students in thinking about an area model. Ask:

- *What does it mean to find $\frac{1}{3}$ of $\frac{2}{3}$?*

- *When you find $\frac{1}{3}$ of $\frac{2}{3}$, should you get something greater than or less than $\frac{2}{3}$?*

These questions are to get students thinking about what happens when they multiply fractions.

Read through the problem with your class. Point out that they are to figure out what part, or fraction, of the whole brownie pan is being bought.

- *As you work on this problem, think about the size of the answer when you are finding a part of a part. Questions A, B, and C ask you to draw models to show how the brownie pan might look before a customer buys part of what is left. Then you need to mark the part in the brownie pan to show how much the customer buys.*

Provide students with Labsheet 3.1 for drawing models.

Working in pairs or small groups is appropriate for this problem.

Explore 3.1

As you circulate, ask students what it means to find a fraction of something, such as $\frac{1}{2}$ of $\frac{3}{4}$. Be sure they make drawings for Questions A–C. Note whether students are naming the fraction of the *whole pan* that is being bought.

Suggested Questions

- *How does your drawing help someone see the part of the whole pan that is bought? What could you do in your drawing to make this clearer?*

If students should happen to notice that they can multiply the numerators and multiply the denominators, ask them to use their drawings to show why they think this works.

Ask about students' estimation strategies when they are working on Question D. If students are finding exact answers, redirect them. For example, with part (1):

- *What is $\frac{5}{6}$ of 1 whole?* (part of a whole, or $\frac{5}{6}$)

- *Does this help you estimate whether $\frac{5}{6} \times 1$ is greater than or less than 1?* (Yes, it is less than 1.)

- *Now think about $1 \times \frac{1}{2}$. Is this greater than 1?* (no)

- *Is it greater than $\frac{1}{2}$?* (no)

- *So is $\frac{5}{6} \times \frac{1}{2}$ greater than $\frac{1}{2}$?* (No. You have just $\frac{5}{6}$ of $\frac{1}{2}$, which is less than $\frac{1}{2}$.)

As groups finish, you may want to have large sheets of paper or sheets of blank transparency film available for groups to share their drawings.

Summarize 3.1

For Questions A–C, have groups share their solutions and strategies. Focus the conversation on taking a "part of a part." Help them connect what is happening in the drawing to what is happening in the problem.

Suggested Questions

- *How did you decide what fraction of the whole pan is being bought?* (I had thirds and broke them into halves. A half of a third is a sixth.)

- *Can someone share a way to mark the brownie pan so it is easy to see what part of the whole pan is bought?* (Here is an opportunity to suggest that using horizontal and vertical lines makes it clear what is happening. If someone does not suggest this approach, do so yourself.)

- *What number sentence could I write for Question A?* ($\frac{1}{2} \times \frac{2}{3} = \frac{2}{6}$)

It is helpful to write the number sentence by the models. By doing this, students typically notice that you can multiply the numerators and denominators to find the product. If this idea is raised, push students to explain why it works.

- *Why does multiplying numerators and denominators work?*

Students might point out that the numbers give the right answer. If students do, direct them to consider both the numbers and the brownie pans.

- *For Question A, how did you first mark your brownie pan?* (into thirds, as in Part 1 of the diagram in the next column)

- *When you took half of the thirds you broke each third into two parts. How many parts were in the whole after you did this?* (six)

- *What part of your fractions told you to make thirds and then halves?* (the denominators)

- *What does the denominator of a fraction tell you?* (how many parts are in the whole)

- *What part of your drawing in Question A shows the denominator?* (The picture drawn for Part 2 below. The whole pan is marked into a 2 by 3 array with 6 sections in all.)

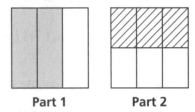

Part 1   **Part 2**

- *So multiplying the denominators gives the number of parts in the marking of the whole. Your numerators are 2 and 1. Where do you see this on the brownie pan drawing?* (It is two of the thirds inside one of the halves. See figure below.)

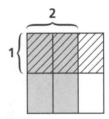

- *After you draw in your lines can you see that the shaded area is 1 by 2 or 2 of the total parts? What does the numerator of a fraction tell you?* (How many parts of the whole are being bought. This is 1×2 of 2 parts of the whole.)

Students will not grasp this idea right away but continue to ask about it when appropriate. We want students to realize that there is a reason that they can multiply the numerators and multiply the denominators to find the product.

Once students seem to understand how to find the fractions of fractions that were purchased, talk about the cost of the brownies in Questions A and B. Ask students to explain how they arrived at their answers.

Finish up by having students share their estimation strategies in Question D. Be sure to focus the conversation on how students decided if each product was greater than or less than 1 and greater than or less than each of the factors.

- *In Question D, part (2), if you have $\frac{5}{6}$ of a whole brownie pan, do you have less than, more than, or exactly a whole pan? (Less than; $\frac{5}{6}$ is less than 1 whole.)*

- *What about $\frac{5}{6}$ of $\frac{2}{3}$ of the pan? Is this larger or smaller than a whole pan of brownies? (smaller)*

Below are some possible ways to reason about each part in Question D:

1. If you have $\frac{5}{6}$ of something, you do not have all of it, so $\frac{5}{6}$ of $\frac{1}{2}$ will be only a part of the $\frac{1}{2}$. This means that it is less than 1.

2. $\frac{5}{6}$ of 1 is a part of 1, so it is less than 1.

3. $\frac{5}{6}$ is almost a whole. If you have two $\frac{5}{6}$ parts, you have more than 1.

4. $\frac{3}{7}$ is less than $\frac{1}{2}$. If you have two parts that are less than $\frac{1}{2}$, you have less than 1.

5. $\frac{3}{4}$ of something that is less than 1 means that you will get a part, not all, of something already less than 1.

6. $\frac{9}{3}$ is 3 and $\frac{1}{2}$ of 3 is $1\frac{1}{2}$, which is greater than 1.

7. $\frac{10}{7}$ is $1\frac{3}{7}$ or a little less than $1\frac{1}{2}$. If you take $\frac{1}{2}$ of $1\frac{1}{2}$, you will have less than 1.

8. Again, $\frac{10}{7}$ is $1\frac{3}{7}$ or a little less than $1\frac{1}{2}$. $\frac{9}{10}$ is almost a whole, so $\frac{9}{10} \times 1\frac{1}{2}$ will be almost all of $1\frac{1}{2}$. You will have more than 1.

3.1

How Much of the Pan Have We Sold?

Mathematical Goals

- Estimate products of fractions
- Use models to represent the product of two fractions
- Understand that finding a fraction *of* a number means multiplication

Launch

- *Can you describe some situations where multiplication is used?*

Discuss the football-packing problem in the introduction to the investigation in the Student Edition to assess what students know about fraction multiplication situations. Do students have any sense of how big or small the products are?

Use the Paulo and Shania problem to engage students in thinking about an area model. Ask:

- *What does it mean to find $\frac{1}{3}$ of $\frac{2}{3}$? When you find $\frac{1}{3}$ of $\frac{2}{3}$, should you get something greater than or less than $\frac{2}{3}$?*

Read the problem and point out that they are to figure out what part, or fraction, of the whole brownie pan is being bought.

- *As you work on this problem, think about the size of the answer when you are finding a part of a part. Questions A, B, and C ask you to draw models to show how the brownie pan might look before a customer buys part of what is left. Then you need to mark the part in the brownie pan to show how much the customer buys.*

Provide students with Labsheet 3.1. Have students work in pairs or small groups.

Explore

As you circulate, ask students what it means to find a fraction of something, such as $\frac{1}{2}$ of $\frac{3}{4}$. Note whether students are naming the fraction of the *whole pan* that is being bought.

If students notice that they can multiply the numerators and multiply the denominators, ask them to use their drawings to show why this works.

Ask students about their estimation strategies in Question D. If students are finding exact answers, redirect them.

Materials

- Labsheet 3.1
- Two different colored pencils

As students share how they marked the brownie pan and their solutions for Questions A–C, focus the conversation on taking a part of a part.

- *How did you decide what fraction of a whole pan is being bought?*
- *Can someone share a way to mark the brownie pan so it is easy to see what part of the whole pan is being bought?*
- *What number sentence could I write for Question A?*

It is helpful to write number sentences by the models. Typically, students notice that you can multiply the numerators and the denominators to find the product. If this idea is raised, push students to explain why it works.

Have students share their estimation strategies for Question D. Focus on how students decided if each product was greater than or less than one.

Materials
- Student notebooks

ACE Assignment Guide for Problem 3.1

Differentiated Instruction
Solutions for All Learners

Core 1–3, 36, 37
Other *Applications* 4, 5

Adapted For suggestions about adapting ACE exercises, see the CMP *Special Needs Handbook*.
Connecting to Prior Units 37: *Bits and Pieces I*

Answers to Problem 3.1

A. 1. Possible model:

2. Possible model:

3. $\frac{2}{6}$, or $\frac{1}{3}$, of a pan; $\frac{1}{3}$ of \$12.00, or \$4.00.

B. 1. Possible model:

2. Possible model:

3. $\frac{3}{8}$ of a pan; $\frac{3}{8}$ of \$12.00, or \$4.50.

C. 1. $\frac{1}{12}$

2. $\frac{2}{12}$, or $\frac{1}{6}$

3. $\frac{3}{12}$, or $\frac{1}{4}$

4. $\frac{6}{20}$, or $\frac{3}{10}$

D. 1. less than 1

2. less than 1

3. greater than 1

4. less than 1

5. less than 1

6. greater than 1

7. less than 1

8. greater than 1

Goals

- Estimate products of fractions
- Use models to represent the product of two fractions
- Understand that finding a fraction *of* a number means multiplication

A linear model is introduced to connect to an important mathematical idea from *Bits and Pieces I*—partitioning. In making and using fraction strips, students repeatedly cut a *whole* into smaller, equal-sized pieces.

The introduction to the problem revisits the fundraising thermometers and has diagrams of thermometers turned on their side like fraction strips. Note that the actual problem uses number lines.

The model used in the Getting Ready is only one approach to the problem $\frac{1}{4} \times \frac{2}{3}$. This approach leads to the answer with the least common denominator. The alternative approach below leads to twelfths as the unit rather than sixths. In this approach, you first partition a thermometer or number line into thirds and label the thirds.

To find $\frac{1}{4}$ of $\frac{2}{3}$, each third can be partitioned into fourths. If you partition the number line this way, there will be four sections in each third or $3 \times 4 = 12$ parts in the whole.

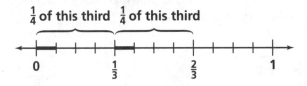

Since you need $\frac{1}{4}$ of $\frac{2}{3}$, you will need 1 of the 4 parts in each of the two thirds, or $1 \times 2 = 2$ of the twelfths in the whole.

When students are working on the problem, they can use brownie pan or number line models. Look for examples of both to use in the summary. Both models are useful because each seems more natural in different situations. Question A, part (4), highlights this idea by asking students to think about contexts where each model makes sense. Question B uses both linear and area contexts.

Launch 3.2

Use Transparency 3.2 to launch this problem. Work through the example in the problem introduction. Display the interval $\frac{2}{3}$ on the overhead and ask students how they might find $\frac{1}{4}$ of part of the thermometer. They should understand from prior work that the section of the thermometer should be cut into four equal sections and one of these parts is used to represent $\frac{1}{4}$ of $\frac{2}{3}$. Then turn their attention to naming this new part using the Getting Ready.

Suggested Questions

- *We need to divide the whole thermometer into pieces of the same size in order to decide what $\frac{1}{4}$ of $\frac{2}{3}$ is. This is just like the brownie pans where you decided what fraction or part of the whole pan someone bought. Where are 0 and 1 on the thermometer?* (0 is at the far left of the thermometer, and 1 is at the goal line.)

Draw a number line under the thermometer.

- *What part of the whole thermometer is $\frac{1}{4}$ of $\frac{2}{3}$?* ($\frac{1}{6}$)

- *Can you use the thermometer to show that?* (The $\frac{2}{3}$-sized section of the thermometer is divided into four equal parts. When the rest of the thermometer is sectioned into pieces of the same size, there are six pieces. Then $\frac{1}{4}$ of $\frac{2}{3}$ on the thermometer is $\frac{1}{6}$ of the distance from 0 to 1.)

- *How would you represent $\frac{1}{4}$ of $\frac{2}{3}$ on a number line?* (Students should describe the same approach as used for the thermometer but on a number line that is marked with 0 and 1.)

- *How would you represent $\frac{3}{4}$ of $\frac{2}{3}$ on a number line?* (Students should describe a similar procedure as the one used with $\frac{1}{4} \times \frac{2}{3}$, but they will need to figure out how to name the part of the whole representing $\frac{3}{4}$ of the $\frac{2}{3}$. They need to partition the distance from 0 to 1 into six parts. $\frac{3}{4}$ of the $\frac{2}{3}$ length is the same as $\frac{1}{2}$ of the distance from 0 to 1.)

As you work through how to model problems, point out the importance of labeling the number lines so it is possible to keep track of where the original thirds are. Read through the problem with the students. Question A asks students to estimate before they find the exact answer. Remind students that they can use their estimate as a guide for a reasonable answer when they compute.

Problem 3.2 is a rather long problem. You might stop and summarize Question A, then assign Questions B–D for homework and summarize the whole problem the next day.

Provide students with markers and blank transparencies on which to write their word problems. Have them work in small groups.

Explore 3.2

Look for examples of models to discuss in the summary.

Support students who need help labeling their models so they can keep track of the different partitioning. You might suggest that they use two colors with number line models as well as brownie pan models.

Suggested Questions If students are struggling, guide them through some additional examples such as the following.

- *Let's look at $\frac{1}{5} \times \frac{2}{3}$. How would you start if you wanted to use a number line model?*

(Draw a number line, and label 0 and 1. Next, partition the number line into thirds, and mark $\frac{1}{3}$ and $\frac{2}{3}$.)

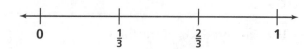

- *How could you repartition to find $\frac{1}{5}$ of $\frac{2}{3}$?* (You could break each third into five equal parts.)

- *Does this relate to folding fraction strips in* Bits and Pieces I? (yes) *When you had a thirds strip and you folded each third into five parts, what kind of fraction strip did you make?* (fifteenths)

- *What is $\frac{1}{5}$ of two thirds?* (Each $\frac{1}{5}$ of one third is $\frac{1}{15}$, so twice that would be $\frac{2}{15}$.)

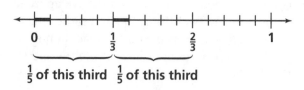

$\frac{1}{5}$ of this third $\frac{1}{5}$ of this third

- *What if I wanted to find $\frac{3}{5}$ of $\frac{2}{3}$?* (You would take three fifths from each of the two thirds. When you think about the whole fraction strip, a number line from 0 to 1, you are really taking three fifteenths from each of the thirds. So, $\frac{3}{5} \times \frac{2}{3} = \frac{6}{15}$.)

As groups finish you might want to have long sheets of paper or blank transparencies available to share their drawings.

Summarize 3.2

Have students share the reasoning they used to estimate the products in Question A. As students share their models and solutions, help them use estimation to decide if their models and computations are reasonable. One way to organize the discussion of part (1) is to have students share their estimates, models, and solution processes for parts (a) and (b) first. When discussing part (b), have students share their word problems also.

Suggested Questions Ask questions such as these:

- *Does Samantha's estimate for part (1a) seem reasonable?*
- *Did anyone reason a different way?*
- *Lee used a brownie pan model for part (1a). Who can share a number line model?*

After discussing parts (1a) and (1b), ask:

- *In part (1a), we are finding $\frac{1}{3}$ of $\frac{1}{2}$, and in part (1b), we are finding $\frac{2}{3}$ of $\frac{1}{2}$. How are the answers in these two parts related?* (The answer to $\frac{2}{3}$ of $\frac{1}{2}$ is twice as great.)
- *What do you think is $\frac{4}{3}$ of $\frac{1}{2}$?* (It is four times as great as the answer to $\frac{1}{3}$ of $\frac{1}{2}$.)

Question A, part (3), and Question C both prompt students to look for patterns and think about a strategy for multiplying fractions by fractions.

See Figure 1 for some beginning algorithms that students have suggested.

If the strategy of multiplying numerators and multiplying denominators emerges here, see Summary 3.1 for a suggested way to handle the conversation. To raise the issue, list the number sentences solved so far on the board (e.g. $\frac{2}{3} \times 2\frac{1}{2} = \frac{2}{6}$), then ask:

- *What patterns do you see between the fraction numerators and denominators and their products?* (You can just multiply numerators and denominators.)
- *But the real question is, why does this work?* (Take student ideas and use the modeling in Summary 3.1 or the Mathematics of the Unit section to help guide the students.)

For Question D, have students present their reactions to Ian and Libby's conversation.

- *Does multiplying two numbers always lead to a greater product? Why?*
- *Can you give an example that shows what Libby is talking about?*
- *Does multiplication with fractions always lead to a product that is less than each factor?*

Do not expect students to resolve this last question. They will explore this idea in the problems that follow.

Figure 1

Problem	Students' solutions and explanation	
$\frac{5}{8} \times 12$	Solution:	$12 \div 8$ pieces $\times 5 = 1\frac{1}{2} \times 5 = 7\frac{1}{2}$
	Explanation:	12 divided into 8 pieces; take 5
$\frac{1}{2} \times \frac{2}{3}$	Solution:	Just $\frac{1}{3}$. When the denominator of the first number is equal to the numerator of the second number, just use the first number for the numerator and the second number for the denominator.
	Explanation:	You have 2 pieces and need 1 of the 2 pieces.
$\frac{1}{2} \times$ any number	Solution:	$\frac{1}{2} \times \frac{3}{8} = \frac{3}{16}$
	Explanation:	Double the denominator because you are making pieces one-half as large, or two times smaller.
$\frac{1}{2} \times 2\frac{2}{3}$	Solution:	$\frac{1}{2} \times 2 = 1$ and $\frac{1}{2} \times \frac{2}{3} = \frac{1}{3}$, so the sum is $1\frac{1}{3}$
	Explanation:	Break up the number into 2 and $\frac{2}{3}$; then multiply each part and add. (Distributive property)

3.2

Finding a Part of a Part

Mathematical Goals

- Estimate products of fractions
- Use models to represent the product of two fractions
- Understand that finding a fraction *of* a number means multiplication

Launch

Work through the thermometer problem and the Getting Ready in the introduction. Use Transparency 3.2.

- *Where are 0 and 1 on the thermometer? What part of the whole thermometer is $\frac{1}{4}$ of $\frac{2}{3}$? Use the thermometer to show that.*
- *How would you represent $\frac{1}{4}$ of $\frac{2}{3}$ on a number line?*
- *How would you represent $\frac{3}{4}$ of $\frac{2}{3}$ on a number line?*

As you work through how to model problems, point out the importance of labeling number lines so you keep track where the original thirds are.

Read through the problem. Remind students that they can use their estimates as a guide. Have students work in small groups.

Materials
- Transparency 3.2

Explore

Look for examples of models to discuss in the summary.

Support students who need help labeling their models so they can keep track of the different partitioning.

Provide groups with large sheets of paper or transparencies to share their drawings.

Materials
- Large sheets of paper or blank transparencies (optional)
- Marker (optional)

Summarize

One way to organize the discussion is to have students share their estimates, models, and solution processes for Question A, parts (1a) and (1b). When discussing part (1b), have students share their word problems.

- *In part (1a), we are finding $\frac{1}{3}$ of $\frac{1}{2}$, and in part (1b), we are finding $\frac{2}{3}$ of $\frac{1}{2}$. How are the answers in these parts related?*

If the idea of multiplying numerators and denominators did not come out in Problem 3.1, push for it here.

- *What patterns do you see between the numerators and denominators and their products? Why does this work?*

Have students share their reactions to Ian and Libby's conversation in Question D.

Materials
- Student notebooks

continued on next page

• *Does multiplying two numbers always lead to a greater product?*

• *Does multiplication with fractions always lead to a product that is less than each factor?*

ACE Assignment Guide for Problem 3.2

Core 6–8, 10, 38, 39

Other *Applications* 9; unassigned choices from previous problems

Adapted For suggestions about adapting Exercise 6 and other ACE exercises, see the CMP *Special Needs Handbook*.

Answers to Problem 3.2

A. 1. a. less than $\frac{1}{2}$ **b.** less than $\frac{1}{2}$

    c. less than $\frac{1}{2}$ **d.** greater than $\frac{1}{2}$

2. a. $\frac{1}{3} \times \frac{1}{2} = \frac{1}{6}$

Area Model: **Number-Line Model:**

 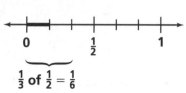

$\frac{1}{3}$ of $\frac{1}{2} = \frac{1}{6}$

b. $\frac{2}{3} \times \frac{1}{2} = \frac{2}{6}$, or $\frac{1}{3}$

Area Model: **Number-Line Model:**

 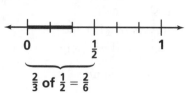

$\frac{2}{3}$ of $\frac{1}{2} = \frac{2}{6}$

c. $\frac{1}{8} \times \frac{4}{5} = \frac{4}{40}$, or $\frac{1}{10}$

Area Model: **Number-Line Model:**

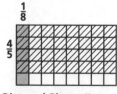 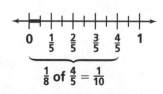

$\frac{1}{8}$ of $\frac{4}{5} = \frac{1}{10}$

d. $\frac{5}{6} \times \frac{3}{4} = \frac{15}{24}$, or $\frac{5}{8}$

Area Model: **Number-Line Model:**

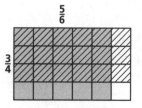 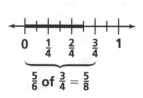

$\frac{5}{6}$ of $\frac{3}{4} = \frac{5}{8}$

3. Answers will vary. Students may notice that they can multiply numerators and multiply denominators to find the product of two fractions.

4. a. Answers will vary. Check to see if the context is one where it would make sense to use a brownie pan model. Question B part (2) is an example of a situation where it would make sense to use a brownie pan or area model.

    b. Answers will vary. Check to see if the context is one where it would make sense to use a number line model. Question B, parts (1) and (3) are examples of problems that use a number line or linear model.

B. 1. $\frac{1}{8}$ mile; $\frac{1}{4} \times \frac{1}{2} = \frac{1}{8}$

   2. $\frac{4}{15}$ acre; $\frac{1}{3} \times \frac{4}{5} = \frac{4}{15}$

   3. $\frac{18}{30}$ or $\frac{9}{15}$ or $\frac{3}{5}$ mile; $\frac{2}{3} \times \frac{9}{10} = \frac{18}{30}$ or $\frac{9}{15}$ or $\frac{3}{5}$

C. If you multiply the numerators and multiply the denominators, you will get the product of the fractions.

D. Libby is correct if the factors are both less than 1. When you multiply a fraction less than 1 by a fraction less than 1, you are taking a part of a part. This gives a product that is less than either factor. Ian is correct if both factors are greater than or equal to 1. You might want to explore what happens when one factor is less than 1 and the other is greater than 1, e.g., $\frac{2}{3} \times \frac{7}{4}$. The product is greater than $\frac{2}{3}$ but less than $\frac{7}{4}$.

Goals

- Estimate products of fractions

- Develop and use strategies and models for multiplying combinations of fractions, whole numbers, and mixed numbers to solve problems

- Determine when multiplication is an appropriate operation

The Getting Ready explores estimation in situations where fractions and mixed numbers are multiplied. Students develop strategies for multiplying mixed numbers built on their previous work and use estimation to check the reasonableness of their answers.

There are different ways to approach estimation. For example, with the first problem in the Getting Ready, $\frac{1}{2} \times 2\frac{9}{10}$, students might use a benchmark strategy. Since $2\frac{9}{10}$ is almost 3, a reasonable estimate would be $\frac{1}{2}$ of 3 or $1\frac{1}{2}$. In the second problem, $1\frac{1}{2} \times 2\frac{9}{10}$, students might use a combination of benchmarking and distribution. $1\frac{1}{2} \times 3$ will give a good estimate. In order to find $1\frac{1}{2} \times 3$, some students break apart the $1\frac{1}{2}$ and multiply each part by 3. This can be thought of as $3(1 + \frac{1}{2}) = (3 \times 1) + (3 \times \frac{1}{2})$. This notion of decomposing the fractions will be looked at explicitly in Problem 3.4. The terminology of "distribution" is not important for students to know, but if the strategy surfaces here, be sure students understand how the numbers in the problem are being decomposed (taken apart), operated on, and then recombined. Using notation such as $3(1 + \frac{1}{2}) = (3 \times 1) + (3 \times \frac{1}{2})$ is helpful when you are summarizing.

Creating models for multiplication problems that involve combinations of fractions, whole numbers, and mixed numbers is a bit more complex than fraction times fraction situations. Consider these two problems:

$$\frac{1}{3} \times 2\frac{1}{2} \qquad 2\frac{1}{2} \times \frac{3}{4}$$

Taking $\frac{1}{3}$ of $2\frac{1}{2}$ is different than taking $\frac{1}{3}$ of a fraction such as $\frac{3}{4}$. Here students have to coordinate multiple wholes. An example of an area model for $\frac{1}{3} \times 2\frac{1}{2}$ is shown below.

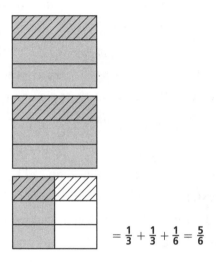

$$= \frac{1}{3} + \frac{1}{3} + \frac{1}{6} = \frac{5}{6}$$

For $2\frac{1}{2} \times \frac{3}{4}$, the area model could be as shown below.

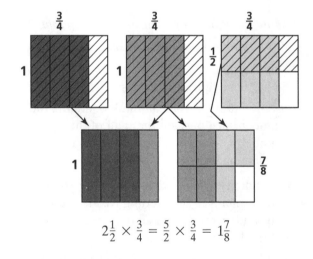

$$2\frac{1}{2} \times \frac{3}{4} = \frac{5}{2} \times \frac{3}{4} = 1\frac{7}{8}$$

Launch 3.3

Introduce the problem by writing $\frac{2}{3} \times 2\frac{2}{5}$ and $2\frac{1}{2} \times 1\frac{1}{3}$ on board. Ask students to explain how each of these is different from the fraction multiplication problems they have solved already.

INVESTIGATION 3

Then use the Getting Ready to explore ways to estimate in mixed number situations. Begin by asking a student to share a strategy.

Suggested Questions

- *What whole number is $2\frac{9}{10}$ nearest?* (3)

- *So the answer to the problem is close to $\frac{1}{2}$ of 3. What is this product?* ($1\frac{1}{2}$)

- *What does this tell you about the product for $\frac{1}{2} \times 2\frac{9}{10}$?* (The product will be about $1\frac{1}{2}$.)

- *Is the actual product closer to 1 or 2?* (Since $2\frac{9}{10}$ is a little less than 3, the exact product will be a little less than $1\frac{1}{2}$ or closer to 1.)

- *Did someone use a different strategy to estmate $\frac{1}{2} \times 2\frac{9}{10}$?*

- *Who can explain how they estimated $1\frac{1}{2} \times 2\frac{9}{10}$?* (First, I wrote $2\frac{9}{10}$ as 3. Since I'm multiplying by $1\frac{1}{2}$, I used the 3 once, and then I added half of 3, or $1\frac{1}{2}$, to get $4\frac{1}{2}$. Since I rounded $2\frac{9}{10}$ up to 3, $4\frac{1}{2}$ will be a little too big. The actual answer will be greater than 4 and not quite $4\frac{1}{2}$.)

- *How is finding $\frac{1}{2}$ of some amount different from finding $1\frac{1}{2}$ of the same amount?* (When you find half of a number you cut the amount in half and your product is smaller. To find $1\frac{1}{2}$ of a number, you can think of adding the number once plus another half of the number. The answer is greater than the original quantity.)

Ask students to share their reasoning about the last two problems in the Getting Ready. Here is one way students might possibly reason about each of the last two problems.

For $2\frac{1}{2} \times \frac{4}{7}$, one could reason that $\frac{4}{7}$ is about $\frac{1}{2}$, and $\frac{1}{2}$ of $2\frac{1}{2}$ is about $1\frac{1}{4}$. The actual answer will be closest to 1 and greater than 1.

For $3\frac{1}{4} \times 2\frac{11}{12}$, one could reason that $3\frac{1}{4}$ is about 3 and $2\frac{11}{12}$ is about 3, so $3 \times 3 = 9$. The actual product is a little more than 9 because

the extra $\frac{1}{4}$ in $3\frac{1}{4}$ will make the product greater than 9.

Explain the directions for Problem 3.3. Make sure the students understand what they are expected to do. Pairs are a good grouping arrangement for this problem.

Explore 3.3

Question A is a fraction times a fraction, which is familiar to the students. However, they may struggle at first when they try to model Questions B–D. If they are unsure, reread the problem to them. You might ask questions like the following:

Suggested Questions

- *What do the $\frac{2}{3}$ and the 16 in Question B represent?*

- *What does it mean when it says "$\frac{2}{3}$ of a 16-ounce bag"?*

- *How do you find $\frac{2}{3}$ of something?*

Look for various models to use in the summary. Provide students with markers and blank transparency film on which to put their diagrams. Ask groups to write the number sentences for the problems on their transparency.

Summarize 3.3

For each problem, begin by discussing the estimates that students made. When students share their models and exact answers, focus on their reasoning.

Suggested Questions After a solution is presented, ask questions like the following:

- *Do you agree with this answer and the reasoning? Explain.*

- *Does your exact answer seem reasonable given the estimate?*

- *Does anyone have a different way to think about the problem?*

The answers to Problem 3.3 provide possible solutions that students might share.

3.3 Modeling More Multiplication Situations

PACING 1 day

Mathematical Goals

- Estimate products of fractions
- Develop and use strategies and models for multiplying combinations of fractions, whole numbers, and mixed numbers to solve problems
- Determine when multiplication is an appropriate operation

Launch

Use the Getting Ready to explore ways to estimate in mixed number situations. Ask a student to share a strategy.

- *What whole number is $2\frac{9}{10}$ nearest?*
- *So the problem becomes $\frac{1}{2}$ of 3. What is the product?*
- *What does this tell you about the product for $\frac{1}{2} \times 2\frac{9}{10}$?*
- *Who can explain how they estimated $1\frac{1}{2} \times 2\frac{9}{10}$?*
- *How is finding $\frac{1}{2}$ of some amount different from finding $1\frac{1}{2}$ of the same amount?*

Read the directions for Problem 3.3, and have students work in pairs.

Materials
- Transparency 3.3

Explore

Question A is a familiar fraction times fraction situation. If students struggle with Questions B–D, read the problem aloud and ask questions:

- *What do the $\frac{2}{3}$ and the 16 in Question B represent?*
- *What does it mean when it says "$\frac{2}{3}$ of a 16-ounce bag"?*
- *How do you find $\frac{2}{3}$ of something?*

Provide markers and blank transparency film on which students can put their drawings and number sentences for the problems.

Materials
- Blank transparencies and markers (optional)

Summarize

For each problem, talk about the estimates and then the exact answers that students made. Focus on their reasoning.

- *Do you agree with this answer and the reasoning?*
- *Does the exact answer seem reasonable given the estimate?*
- *Does anyone have another way to think about the problem?*

Materials
- Student notebooks

ACE Assignment Guide for Problem 3.3

Differentiated Instruction
Solutions for All Learners

Core 11–14, 40–45
Other *Applications* 15, *Extensions* 48; unassigned choices from previous problems

Adapted For suggestions about adapting ACE exercises, see the CMP *Special Needs Handbook*.

Answers to Problem 3.3

A. Possible estimate: Between $\frac{1}{2}$ and $\frac{3}{4}$.

Possible model: Break each eighth into four parts and take or count three of the four in seven of the eighths. (Figure 2)

$\frac{3}{4} \times \frac{7}{8} = \frac{21}{32}$

B. Possible estimate: About 10, since $\frac{2}{3}$ of 15 is 10. Possible models: Many students reason that they will need two $\frac{1}{3}$ sections from each of 16 whole oz, or $2 \times 16 = 32$ thirds, or $10\frac{2}{3}$.

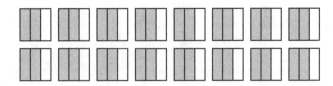

Other students group the 16 oz into sets of 3 and take two out of each set. This gives 10 of 15 oz with one extra whole from which they take two thirds.

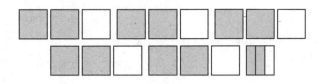

$\frac{2}{3} \times 16 = 10\frac{2}{3}$ oz

C. Possible estimate: A little more than $\frac{2}{3}$.
Possible model: $(\frac{1}{3}$ of 1$)$ + $(\frac{1}{3}$ of 1$)$ + $(\frac{1}{3}$ of $\frac{1}{2})$ = $\frac{1}{3}$ + $\frac{1}{3}$ + $\frac{1}{6}$ = $\frac{5}{6}$ pound.

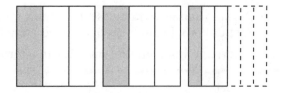

A second approach is to divide the $2\frac{1}{2}$ lb into sixths ($\frac{15}{6} = 2\frac{1}{2}$). One third of 15 sixths is 5 sixths, so $\frac{1}{3}$ of $2\frac{1}{2}$ lb is $\frac{5}{6}$ lb.

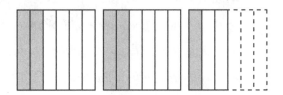

$\frac{1}{3} \times 2\frac{1}{2} = \frac{5}{6}$ pound

D. Possible estimate: A little more than 20. Almost 2 times almost 10 is about 20.

Exact answer: $24\frac{1}{2}$ acres

Possible model: You can repeatedly add $2\frac{1}{3}$ 10 times for the 10 days. Then find $\frac{1}{2}$ of $2\frac{1}{3}$ for the partial day. In essence, this is finding $(10 \times 2\frac{1}{3}) + (\frac{1}{2} \times 2\frac{1}{3})$.

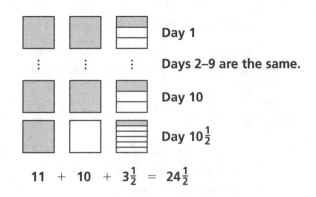

Day 1

Days 2–9 are the same.

Day 10

Day 10$\frac{1}{2}$

11 + 10 + 3$\frac{1}{2}$ = 24$\frac{1}{2}$

$2\frac{1}{3} \times 10\frac{1}{2}$ or $(2\frac{1}{3} \times 10) + (2\frac{1}{3} \times \frac{1}{2}) = 24\frac{1}{2}$ acres

Figure 2

1 | 1/8 2/8 3/8 4/8 5/8 6/8 7/8 1

3.4 Changing Forms

Goals

- Explore the relationships between two numbers and their product

- Develop and use algorithms for multiplying combinations of fractions, whole numbers, and mixed numbers

Two multiplication strategies are explored in this problem. The strategy introduced in the Getting Ready involves changing the form of mixed numbers and whole numbers so students can operate in the same way as when both factors are fractions. This will allow them to draw on a computational strategy they have already explored. A second strategy is an application of the distributive property and is developed in Question C. Whether this strategy is useful depends upon the actual quantities in the problem. We do not wish to promote it as the only approach to multiplying fractions, but it is a reasonable approach for certain problems. Since many students use it intuitively, and sometimes use it incorrectly, it is important to have a conversation with students around an example.

With whole numbers:
$$8 \times 24 = 8 \times (20 + 4) =$$
$$(8 \times 20) + (8 \times 4) =$$
$$160 + 32 = 192$$

With fractions: $2\frac{1}{2} \times 2\frac{1}{5} = (2 + \frac{1}{2}) \times 2\frac{1}{5} =$
$$(2 \times 2\frac{1}{5}) + (\frac{1}{2} \times 2\frac{1}{5})$$

Mathematics Background

For background on the distributive property in multiplying mixed numbers, see pages 8 and 9.

Launch 3.4

Use the Getting Ready to introduce the notion of changing mixed numbers and whole numbers into fraction form to help in multiplying mixed numbers, whole numbers, and fraction combinations.

Suggested Questions Read through the scenario and pose the following questions.

- *What do you think about Yuri and Paula's conversation? Are the two problems equivalent?* (Yes. $2\frac{2}{3}$ and $\frac{8}{3}$ are equivalent. $2\frac{2}{3}$ is a mixed number and $\frac{8}{3}$ is an improper fraction.)

- *What is the product of $\frac{8}{3} \times \frac{1}{4}$?* ($\frac{8}{12}$)

- *In the last problem, we drew models to multiply with mixed numbers. Take a few minutes and draw a model for this problem.* (Give students time to draw a model. An example is shown below.)

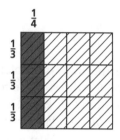

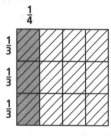

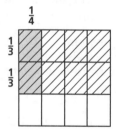

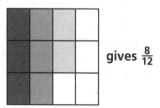

gives $\frac{8}{12}$

- *Who can use their model to prove that the answer $\frac{8}{12}$ is sensible?*

- *In Question A, you are going to use what you know about equivalence to solve multiplication problems. You should first estimate the product to decide if your computation makes sense. Question B asks you to choose two problems and draw a picture to prove your calculations make sense. I am going to assign each group one problem for which to make a diagram and your group can choose the other. Your group is responsible for creating a model that you can use in the summary to talk about your assigned problem.*

Have students work in groups of two to four.

Explore 3.4

Look for pictures for the various problems in Question A. For students who struggle to understand what Question C is suggesting, help them make sense of Takoda's strategy.

Provide each group with blank transparencies on which to record their diagrams for the summary.

Summarize 3.4

Have the group that was assigned part (1) of Question A present their estimate, computation work, and diagram.

Suggested Questions

- *What is a reasonable estimate for $2\frac{1}{2} \times 1\frac{1}{6}$?* (A little more than $2\frac{1}{2}$.)

- *How did you come up with $2\frac{1}{2}$?* (Since $\frac{1}{6}$ is not very big, I changed $1\frac{1}{6}$ to 1 and multiplied $2\frac{1}{2} \times 1$. I estimate that the product will be a little greater than $2\frac{1}{2}$.)

- *Would the estimate of $2\frac{1}{2}$ be an underestimate or an overestimate?* (It would be an underestimate because I rounded $1\frac{1}{6}$ down to 1.)

- *Did anyone estimate a different way?*

- *How did you multiply $2\frac{1}{2} \times 1\frac{1}{6}$?* (I changed each mixed number to a fraction, and then I multiplied the numerators and the denominators. I got $\frac{5}{2} \times \frac{7}{6} = \frac{35}{12} = 2\frac{11}{12}$.)

- *Does this agree with the estimate?*

- *Does the picture you made give you the same product?* (Have students explain their diagrams. Be sure to get students to talk about how the pictures prove the computation work makes sense.)

- *Did anyone reason a different way? Did another group make a diagram of this problem that they can share?*

As you work though the different multiplication problems in Question A, continue to link the diagrams, the estimates, and the computations. Keep your eyes open for students whose diagram actually models the strategy that will be discussed in Question C. Eventually return to the question posed in the Getting Ready box.

- *Do you think Paula's strategy of rewriting the mixed numbers as fractions is sensible?* (Yes.)

Move on to Question C. Ask students to share their interpretation of Takoda's approach. If there are students whose diagrams model this approach you can refer to these to help students better understand what Takoda did. In addition to talking about whether Takoda's strategy will work on parts (2) and (5) in Question A, ask them to think about when it would not be a useful strategy.

- *Would you want to use this strategy on parts (3) or (4)? Why or why not?* (Parts (3) and (4) have fractions in fraction form and whole numbers. There are not any factors that make sense to break apart.)

Some students might suggest that the 16 can be broken up into 10 and 6. Then you can take $\frac{3}{4}$ of 10 and $\frac{3}{4}$ of 6. You might point out that finding $\frac{3}{4}$ of 10 and 6 is not much different from finding $\frac{3}{4}$ of 16.

- *Would you want to use this strategy with the problem $3\frac{7}{8} \times 2\frac{5}{6}$? Why or why not?* (Probably not. Trying to multiply $2\frac{5}{6}$ by 3 and by $\frac{7}{8}$ is probably more work than rewriting the mixed numbers as fractions and multiplying the numerators and denominators.)

The big idea is that some strategies are case-specific. The strategy used in Question C works well in a problem where, for example, a mixed number has $\frac{1}{2}$ as the fraction. This type of problem is often easy to multiply and easy to add the partial products. However, this strategy is not as efficient for a problem such as $3\frac{7}{8} \times 2\frac{5}{6}$.

In Question D, we return to a question posed before—whether multiplication always leads to a product that is greater than each of its factors. In Problem 3.2 it was established that when a fraction less than 1 is multiplied by a fraction less than 1, the product is less than either factor. This leads to the interesting question: When does multiplication lead to a product greater than either factor? This happens when the two factors are both greater than 1.

Challenge

- *Find two factors whose product lies between the two factors on a number line. Explain what kind of factors you need to make this happen and why.* (Multiply a fraction less than 1 by a fraction greater than 1.)

Changing Forms

Mathematical Goals

- Explore the relationships between two numbers and their product
- Develop and use algorithms for multiplying combinations of fractions, whole numbers, and mixed numbers

Launch

Use the Getting Ready to introduce the notion of changing mixed numbers and whole numbers into fraction form to help in multiplying mixed number, whole number, and fraction combinations.

- *What do you think about Yuri and Paula's conversation?*

- *Are the two problems equivalent? What is the product of $\frac{8}{3} \times \frac{1}{4}$?*

- *In the last problem, we drew models to multiply mixed numbers. Take a few minutes to draw a model for this problem.*

- *Who can use their model to prove that $\frac{8}{12}$ is sensible?*

- *In Question, A you are going to use what you know about equivalence to solve multiplication problems. You should estimate the product to see if your computation makes sense. Question B asks you to choose two problems and draw a picture to prove your calculations make sense. I am going to assign each group one problem for which to make a diagram, and let your group choose the other. Your group is responsible for creating a model to use in the summary when you talk about your assigned problem.*

Have students work in groups of two to four.

Materials
- Transparency 3.4

  grid paper

Explore

Look for pictures for the various problems in Question A. For students who struggle to understand what Question C is suggesting, help them make sense of Takoda's strategy.

Provide blank transparencies on which to record diagrams for the summary.

Materials
- Blank transparencies and markers (optional)

Summarize

Have the group assigned part (1) of Question A present their estimate, computation work, and diagram.

- *What is a reasonable estimate for $2\frac{1}{2} \times 1\frac{1}{6}$?*
- *How did you come up with your estimate?*
- *How did you multiply $2\frac{1}{2} \times 1\frac{1}{6}$?*
- *Does this agree with the estimate?*
- *Does the picture you made give you the same product?*

Materials
- Student notebooks

continued on next page

Summarize *continued*

Eventually return to the Getting Ready box.

- *Do you think Paula's strategy of rewriting the mixed numbers as fractions is sensible?*

Move on to Question C. Ask students to share their interpretation of Takota's approach. If there are students whose diagrams model this approach, refer to these to help students better understand what Takota did. In addition, discuss cases, such as parts (2) and (5) of Question A, where this strategy is not very useful.

Use Question D to talk about when multiplication leads to a product greater than or less than each of its factors.

ACE Assignment Guide for Problem 3.4

Differentiated Instruction
Solutions for All Learners

Core 18–20, 46, 47
Other *Applications* 16, 17; *Extensions* 49; unassigned choices from previous problems

Adapted For suggestions about adapting ACE exercises, see the CMP *Special Needs Handbook*.

Answers to Problem 3.4

A. 1. Possible estimate: $2\frac{1}{2} \times 1 = 2\frac{1}{2}$, or a little more than $2\frac{1}{2}$
Actual product: $2\frac{1}{2} \times 1\frac{1}{6} = 2\frac{11}{12}$

2. Possible estimate: $4 \times \frac{1}{4} = 1$, or a little less than 1
Actual product: $3\frac{4}{5} \times \frac{1}{4} = \frac{19}{20}$

3. Possible estimate: $\frac{3}{4} \times 16$ will be between 8 and 16
Actual product: $\frac{3}{4} \times 16 = 12$

4. Possible estimate: $1\frac{1}{2} \times 2 = 3$, or a little more than 3
Actual product: $\frac{5}{3} \times 2 = 3\frac{1}{3}$

5. Possible estimate: $1 \times 4 = 4$, or a little more than 4
Actual product: $1\frac{1}{3} \times 3\frac{6}{7} = 5\frac{1}{7}$

6. Possible estimate: $\frac{1}{4} \times 2 = \frac{1}{2}$, or a little more than $\frac{1}{2}$
Actual product: $\frac{1}{4} \times \frac{9}{4} = \frac{9}{16}$

B. Diagrams will vary.

C. 1. Yes. Takota broke the $2\frac{1}{2}$ into two parts and multiplied $1\frac{1}{6}$ separately by each part. First he multiplied $1\frac{1}{6}$ by 2, and then he multiplied $1\frac{1}{6}$ times $\frac{1}{2}$. Then he took these two products and added them to find the total product.

2. Solution to part (2): $(3 \times \frac{1}{4}) + (\frac{4}{5} \times \frac{1}{4}) = \frac{3}{4} + \frac{1}{5} = \frac{19}{20}$

Solution to part (5): $(1 \times 3\frac{6}{7}) + (\frac{1}{3} \times 3\frac{6}{7}) = 3\frac{6}{7} + 1\frac{2}{7} = 5\frac{1}{7}$

This strategy works because multiplying by a mixed number (such as $2\frac{1}{2}$) is the same as multiplying by the whole number (2) and fraction $(\frac{1}{2})$ separately and the adding each product together.

D. 1. Any fraction between 0 and 1 will give a product between 0 and $1\frac{1}{2}$.

2. N must be 1 or equivalent to 1. (1 or $\frac{2}{2}, \frac{3}{3}, \frac{4}{4}$, etc.)

3. Any number greater than 1 and less than $1\frac{1}{3}$ will give a product between $1\frac{1}{2}$ and 2.

4. When you multiply two fractions less than 1, the product will always be less than of the factors.

5. If you multiply two factors, each of which is greater than 1, the product will be greater than either factor.

Writing a Multiplication Algorithm

Goal

- Develop and use an efficient algorithm to solve any fraction multiplication problem

This problem takes a form somewhat like Problem 2.4 where students looked at pre-sorted addition and subtraction problems in order to develop an algorithm. In Question A, the multiplication problems in each group have something in common. As was the case with addition and subtraction, each case is meant to bring out a special case of multiplication, as follows:

Group 1: Both factors are fractions
Group 2: Factors are combinations of fractions, mixed numbers, and whole numbers
Group 3: Both factors are mixed numbers

Question B provides problems to practice using the multiplication algorithms. Question C provides additional multiplication practice and looks at the result of multiplying a number by its reciprocal. The term reciprocal is not introduced in the problem itself. Rather, a Did You Know? is provided to use when summarizing the problem.

Launch 3.5

Revisit what happened in Problem 2.4 with the class. Remind them how they decided what the addition problems in each group had in common, how they wrote problems that belonged in each group, and how they developed an algorithm for adding any fraction problem.

Look over Problem 3.5. Point out that Question A is like the addition situation in Problem 2.4. Question B has problems for practicing the algorithm they develop, and Question C asks them to explore a special multiplication situation. Students should individually work out all the computation problems in the table in Question A, part (1), then work in small groups to complete the rest of the problem.

Explore 3.5

As students work, pay attention to their work with the groups of problems.

Suggested Questions Ask students questions that will help them to be explicit about what they think each group has in common.

- *What do these problems all have in common?*
- *What are you thinking about naming this category?*
- *Show me a problem that doesn't fit in this category. Why?*
- *What method did you use to solve the problem? Why do you think this method works?*

The purpose of these questions is to help students identify more specifically the mathematical similarities among the problems. Ask these questions even when the description of a group seems obvious.

When groups struggle to write an algorithm for a particular category, ask them questions to ascertain whether the difficulty is not knowing how to solve the problems in the category, difficulty with the idea of an algorithm, or something else.

Check to see which students have a pattern to share in Question C. If students notice that all of the problems have a product of 1, push them to try and figure out why.

Suggested Question

- *Look at the work you did when you found the product for each problem. Why does it make sense that the product is always 1?*

Summarize 3.5

If groups have put their final work on large sheets of paper or transparencies, these can be shared with the class. Several students may offer the traditional algorithm of multiplying the numerators together and multiplying the denominators together. Be sure they talk about how this is done when one or both of the factors is a mixed number or whole number. Some students may use the traditional algorithm but also develop special rules for special situations. For example, they may suggest that when you have a unit fraction and a whole number where the denominator is a factor of the whole number (such as $\frac{1}{5} \times 15$), you can divide the whole number by the denominator of the unit fraction ($15 \div 5 = 3$).

You may want to develop a master list of the algorithms that are presented. Evaluating whether each algorithm is useable and helpful, and how it compares with other algorithms, will further students' understanding of multiplication of fractions, mixed numbers, and whole numbers.

Depending on your students' fluency with multiplication of fractions, you have a couple of choices of where to focus your summary conversation. If you feel the bulk of your students are still developing their ability to multiply fractions, you may want to focus your summary on deciding which of the algorithms written by their classmates work and which ones don't work. If your students have better mastery of their algorithms, you could instead compare these algorithms with those written for addition. Ask, for example, why we need common denominators to add, but don't need them to multiply.

Question C and the Did You Know? that follows Problem 3.5 provide a context to introduce the term reciprocal. Have students share what they think the pattern is and an example of a problem that fits the pattern. Students may notice that the product of each problem is 1 but not notice why this is happening. Be sure to ask questions that push them to figure out why the product is always 1.

After the class discussion, you might ask students to take their algorithm home and ask a family member to try to follow it.

3.5 Writing a Multiplication Algorithm

Mathematical Goal

- Develop and use an efficient algorithm to solve any fraction multiplication problem

Launch

Revisit what happened in Problem 2.4. Remind students how they decided what the addition problems in each group had in common, how they wrote problems that belonged in each group, and how they developed an algorithm for adding any fraction problem.

Look over Problem 3.5. Point out that Question A is like the addition problem in Problem 2.4. Question B has problems for practicing the algorithm, and Question C asks them to explore a special multiplication situation. Students should individually work out all the computation problems in the table in Question A, part (1), then work in small groups to complete the rest of the problem.

Materials
- Transparency 3.5

Vocabulary
- algorithm (revisited)

Explore

Ask questions that will help students identify more specifically the mathematical similarities among the problems. Ask these questions even when the description of a group seems obvious.

When groups struggle to write an algorithm for a particular category, ask questions to ascertain whether the difficulty is not knowing how to solve the problems in the category, difficulty with the idea of an algorithm, or something else.

- *Look at the work you did when you multiplied each problem. How can you explain that the product is always 1?*

Have students put their algorithms on chart paper or transparencies.

Materials
- Large sheets of chart paper or blank transparency film
- Markers

Summarize

Students may offer the traditional algorithm of multiplying numerators and multiplying denominators. Be sure to talk about how this is done when one or both of the factors is a mixed number or whole number. Some students may use the traditional algorithm but develop special rules for special cases.

You may want to develop a master list of algorithms that are presented. Evaluating whether each algorithm is useable and helpful, and how it compares with other algorithms, will further students' understanding of fractions, mixed numbers, and whole numbers.

Materials
- Student notebooks

Vocabulary
- reciprocal

continued on next page

Depending on your students' fluency with multiplication of fractions, you have a couple of choices. For some students, you may want to focus on deciding which algorithms work and which don't. If students have better mastery of their algorithms, you could push students to compare these algorithms with the ones they wrote for addition.

Question C and the Did You Know? that follows Problem 3.5 provide a context to introduce the term reciprocal. Ask students to share what they think the pattern is and an example of a problem that fits the pattern. Students may notice the product for each problem is 1 but not know why this is happening. Be sure to ask questions that push them to figure out why the product is always 1.

ACE Assignment Guide for Problem 3.5

Core 21–33
Other *Applications* 34, 35; unassigned choices from previous problems

Adapted For suggestions about adapting ACE exercises, see the CMP *Special Needs Handbook*.

Answers to Problem 3.5

A. 1.

Group 1	Group 2	Group 3
$\frac{3}{12}$ or $\frac{1}{4}$	$3\frac{3}{4}$	$5\frac{1}{2}$
$\frac{2}{20}$ or $\frac{1}{10}$	$4\frac{4}{5}$	$6\frac{3}{8}$
$\frac{10}{21}$	$8\frac{1}{4}$	$3\frac{1}{5}$

2. Group 1: Both factors are fractions less than 1.
Group 2: Factors are combinations of proper fractions, mixed numbers, and whole numbers.
Group 3: Both factors are mixed numbers.

3. Answers will vary.

4. Answers will vary but should include an efficient strategy for multiplying fractions. For example, one could suggest multiplying the numerators by the numerators and multiplying the denominators and

denominators. In addition, they should include how to deal with situations where one or more of the factors is a mixed number or a whole number.

B. 1. $\frac{5}{6} \times \frac{3}{4} = \frac{15}{24}$, or $\frac{5}{8}$

2. $1\frac{2}{3} \times 12 = 20$

3. $\frac{14}{3} \times \frac{10}{3} = 15\frac{5}{9}$

4. $\frac{2}{5} \times 1\frac{1}{2} = \frac{3}{5}$

C. Each multiplication problem has a product of 1. In each, the second factor is the same as the first factor except that the numerator and denominator are switched. For example, in part (1), you have $\frac{7}{8}$ and $\frac{8}{7}$. This is also the case in part (3) if you rename $1\frac{2}{3}$ as $\frac{5}{3}$ and in part (4) if you rename 11 as $\frac{11}{1}$. Examples of other problems will vary.

The student edition pages for this
investigation begin on the next page.

Notes _____

_____

_____

_____

Investigation 3

Multiplying With Fractions

Sometimes, instead of adding or subtracting fractions, you need to multiply them. For example, suppose you take inventory at the sporting goods store where you work. There are $13\frac{1}{2}$ boxes of footballs in the stock room, and there are 12 footballs in a full box. How can you find the total number of footballs without opening all the boxes? This situation requires multiplication.

In this investigation, you will relate what you already know about multiplication to situations involving fractions. Remember, to make sense of a situation you can draw a model or change a fraction to an equivalent form. You can also estimate to see if your answer makes sense.

3.1 How Much of the Pan Have We Sold?

Paulo and Shania work the brownie booth at the school fair. Sometimes, they have to find a fractional part of another fraction.

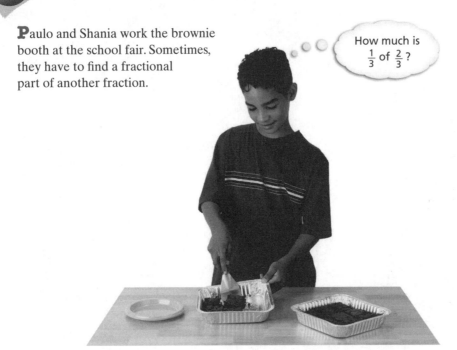

How much is $\frac{1}{3}$ of $\frac{2}{3}$?

32 Bits and Pieces II

STUDENT PAGE

Notes _____

_____

_____

_____

Problem 3.1 A Model for Multiplication

All the pans of brownies are square. A pan of brownies costs \$12. You can buy any fractional part of a pan of brownies and pay that fraction of \$12. For example, $\frac{1}{2}$ of a pan costs $\frac{1}{2}$ of \$12.

A. Mr. Williams asks to buy $\frac{1}{2}$ of a pan that is $\frac{2}{3}$ full.

1. Use a copy of the brownie pan model shown at the right. Draw a picture to show how the brownie pan might look before Mr. Williams buys his brownies.
2. Use a different colored pencil to show the part of the brownies that Mr. Williams buys. Note that Mr. Williams buys *a part of a part* of the brownie pan.
3. What fraction of a whole pan does Mr. Williams buy? What does he pay?

Model of a Brownie Pan

B. Aunt Serena buys $\frac{3}{4}$ of another pan that is half full.

1. Draw a picture to show how the brownie pan might look before Aunt Serena buys her brownies.
2. Use a different colored pencil to show the part of the brownies that Aunt Serena buys.
3. What fraction of a whole pan does Aunt Serena buy? How much did she pay?

C. When mathematicians write $\frac{1}{2}$ of $\frac{1}{4}$, they mean the operation of multiplication, or $\frac{1}{2} \times \frac{1}{4}$. When you multiply a fraction by a fraction, you are finding "a part of a part." Think of each example below as a brownie-pan problem in which you are buying part of a pan that is partly full—a part of a part.

1. $\frac{1}{3} \times \frac{1}{4}$
2. $\frac{1}{4} \times \frac{2}{3}$
3. $\frac{1}{3} \times \frac{3}{4}$
4. $\frac{3}{4} \times \frac{2}{5}$

D. Use estimation to decide if each product is greater than or less than 1. To help, use the "of" interpretation for multiplication. For example, in part (1), think "$\frac{5}{6}$ of $\frac{1}{2}$."

1. $\frac{5}{6} \times \frac{1}{2}$
2. $\frac{5}{6} \times 1$
3. $\frac{5}{6} \times 2$
4. $\frac{3}{7} \times 2$
5. $\frac{3}{4} \times \frac{3}{4}$
6. $\frac{1}{2} \times \frac{9}{3}$
7. $\frac{1}{2} \times \frac{10}{7}$
8. $\frac{9}{10} \times \frac{10}{7}$

ACE Homework starts on page 40.

STUDENT PAGE

STUDENT PAGE

Notes

3.2 Finding a Part of a Part

In *Bits and Pieces I*, you used thermometers to show what fraction of a fundraising goal had been met. These thermometers are like number lines. You mark thermometers in the same way you mark number lines to show parts of parts and to name the resulting piece. The fundraising thermometers can help you make sense of the number lines you will use in this problem.

One sixth-grade class raises $\frac{2}{3}$ of their goal in four days. They wonder what fraction of the goal they raise each day on average. To figure this out, they find $\frac{1}{4}$ of $\frac{2}{3}$. One student makes the drawings shown below:

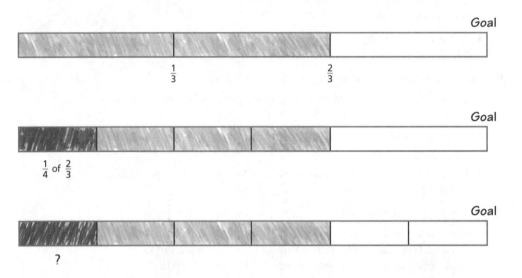

Getting Ready for Problem 3.2

The student above divides the fraction of the goal $\left(\frac{2}{3}\right)$ that is met in four days into fourths to find the length equal to $\frac{1}{4}$ of $\frac{2}{3}$. To figure out the new length, the student divides the whole thermometer into pieces of the same size.

What part of the whole thermometer is $\frac{1}{4}$ of $\frac{2}{3}$?

How would you represent $\frac{1}{4} \times \frac{2}{3}$ on a number line?

How would you represent $\frac{3}{4} \times \frac{2}{3}$ on a number line?

Notes

A. 1. For parts (a)–(d), use estimation to decide if the product is greater than or less than $\frac{1}{2}$.

    a. $\frac{1}{3} \times \frac{1}{2}$ **b.** $\frac{2}{3} \times \frac{1}{2}$ **c.** $\frac{1}{8} \times \frac{4}{5}$ **d.** $\frac{5}{6} \times \frac{3}{4}$

  2. Solve parts (a)–(d) above. Use the brownie-pan model or the number-line model.

  3. What patterns do you see in your work for parts (a)–(d)?

  4. For part (b) above, do each of the following.

    a. Write a word problem where it makes sense to use the brownie-pan model to solve the problem.

    b. Write a word problem where it makes sense to use the number-line model to solve the problem.

B. Solve the following problems. Write a number sentence for each.

  1. Seth runs $\frac{1}{4}$ of a $\frac{1}{2}$-mile relay race. How far does he run?

  2. Mali owns $\frac{4}{5}$ of an acre of land. She uses $\frac{1}{3}$ of it for her dog kennel. How much of an acre is used for the kennel?

  3. Blaine drives the machine that paints stripes along the highway. He plans to paint a stripe that is $\frac{9}{10}$ of a mile long. He is $\frac{2}{3}$ of the way done when he runs out of paint. How long is the stripe he painted?

C. What observations can you make from Questions A and B that help you write an algorithm for multiplying fractions?

D. Ian says, "When you multiply, the product is greater than each of the two numbers you are multiplying: $3 \times 5 = 15$, and 15 is greater than 3 and 5." Libby disagrees. She says, "When you multiply a fraction by a fraction, the product is less than each of the two fractions you multiplied." Who is correct and why?

ACE Homework starts on page 40.

Notes _____

_____

_____

_____

3.3 Modeling More Multiplication Situations

In this problem, you will work with multiplication situations that use fractions, whole numbers, and mixed numbers. It is helpful to estimate first to see if your answer makes sense.

Getting Ready for Problem 3.3

Estimate each product to the nearest whole number $(1, 2, 3, \ldots)$.

$$\frac{1}{2} \times 2\frac{9}{10} \qquad 1\frac{1}{2} \times 2\frac{9}{10} \qquad 2\frac{1}{2} \times \frac{4}{7} \qquad 3\frac{1}{4} \times 2\frac{11}{12}$$

Will the actual product be greater than or less than your whole number estimate?

Problem 3.3 Modeling More Multiplication Situations

For each question:

- Estimate the answer.
- Create a model or a diagram to find the exact answer.
- Write a number sentence.

A. The sixth-graders have a fundraiser. They raise enough money to reach $\frac{7}{8}$ of their goal. Nikki raises $\frac{3}{4}$ of this money. What fraction of the goal does Nikki raise?

B. A recipe calls for $\frac{2}{3}$ of a 16-ounce bag of chocolate chips. How many ounces are needed?

C. Mr. Flansburgh buys a $2\frac{1}{2}$-pound wheel of cheese. His family eats $\frac{1}{3}$ of the wheel. How much cheese have they eaten?

Notes _____

_____

_____

_____

D. Peter and Erin run the corn harvester for Mr. McGreggor. They harvest about $2\frac{1}{3}$ acres each day. They have only $10\frac{1}{2}$ days to harvest the corn. How many acres of corn can they harvest for Mr. McGreggor?

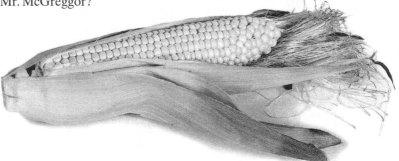

ACE Homework starts on page 40.

3.4 Changing Forms

You have developed some strategies for modeling multiplication and finding products involving fractions. This problem will give you a chance to further develop your strategies. Before you begin a problem, you should always ask yourself: "About how large will the product be?"

Getting Ready for Problem 3.4

Yuri and Paula are trying to find the following product.

$$2\frac{2}{3} \times \frac{1}{4}$$

Yuri says that if he rewrites $2\frac{2}{3}$, he can use what he knows about multiplying fractions. He writes:

$$\frac{8}{3} \times \frac{1}{4}$$

Paula asks, "Can you do that? Are those two problems the same?"

What do you think about Yuri's idea? Are the two multiplication problems equivalent?

Investigation 3 Multiplying With Fractions   **37**

Notes _____

_____

_____

_____

A. Use what you know about equivalence and multiplying fractions to first estimate, and then determine, the following products.

1. $2\frac{1}{2} \times 1\frac{1}{6}$ **2.** $3\frac{4}{5} \times \frac{1}{4}$ **3.** $\frac{3}{4} \times 16$

4. $\frac{5}{3} \times 2$ **5.** $1\frac{1}{3} \times 3\frac{6}{7}$ **6.** $\frac{1}{4} \times \frac{9}{4}$

B. Choose two problems from Question A. Draw a picture to prove that your calculations make sense.

C. Takoda answers Question A part (1) by doing the following:

$$\left(2 \times 1\frac{1}{6}\right) + \left(\frac{1}{2} \times 1\frac{1}{6}\right)$$

1. Do you think Takoda's strategy works? Explain.

2. Try Takoda's strategy on parts (2) and (5) in Question A. Does his strategy work? Why or why not?

D. For parts (1)–(3), find a value for N so that the product of $1\frac{1}{2} \times N$ is:

1. between 0 and $1\frac{1}{2}$ **2.** $1\frac{1}{2}$ **3.** between $1\frac{1}{2}$ and 2

4. Describe when a product will be less than each of the two factors.

5. Describe when a product will be greater than each of the two factors.

ACE **Homework starts on page 40.**

3.5   **Writing a Multiplication Algorithm**

Recall that an algorithm is a reliable mathematical procedure. You have developed algorithms for adding and subtracting fractions. Now you will develop an algorithm for multiplying fractions.

Notes _____

_____

_____

_____

A. 1. Find the products in each group below.

Group 1	Group 2	Group 3
$\frac{1}{3} \times \frac{3}{4}$	$2 \times 1\frac{7}{8}$	$3\frac{2}{3} \times 1\frac{1}{2}$
$\frac{1}{4} \times \frac{2}{5}$	$\frac{2}{5} \times 12$	$2\frac{1}{4} \times 2\frac{5}{6}$
$\frac{2}{3} \times \frac{5}{7}$	$6 \times 1\frac{3}{8}$	$1\frac{1}{5} \times 2\frac{2}{3}$

2. Describe what the problems in each group have in common.

3. Make up one new problem that fits in each group.

4. Write an algorithm that will work for multiplying *any* two fractions, including mixed numbers. Test your algorithm on the problems in the table. If necessary, change your algorithm until you think it will work all the time.

B. Use your algorithm to multiply.

1. $\frac{5}{6} \times \frac{3}{4}$ **2.** $1\frac{2}{3} \times 12$ **3.** $\frac{14}{3} \times \frac{10}{3}$ **4.** $\frac{2}{5} \times 1\frac{1}{2}$

C. Find each product. What pattern do you see? Give another example that fits your pattern.

1. $\frac{7}{8} \times \frac{8}{7}$ **2.** $\frac{1}{9} \times \frac{9}{1}$ **3.** $1\frac{2}{3} \times \frac{3}{5}$ **4.** $11 \times \frac{1}{11}$

ACE **Homework starts on page 40.**

Did You Know?

When you reverse the placement of the numbers in the numerator and the denominator, a new fraction is formed. This new fraction is the **reciprocal** of the original. For example, $\frac{7}{8}$ is the reciprocal of $\frac{8}{7}$, and $\frac{12}{17}$ is the reciprocal of $\frac{17}{12}$, or $1\frac{5}{12}$. Notice that the product of a fraction and its reciprocal is 1.

Investigation 3 Multiplying With Fractions   **39**

Notes _____

_____

_____

_____

Applications

1. Greg buys $\frac{2}{5}$ of a square pan of brownies that has only $\frac{7}{10}$ of the pan left.

   a. Draw a picture of how the brownie pan might look before and after Greg buys his brownies.

   b. What fraction of a whole pan does Greg buy?

2. Ms. Guerdin owns $\frac{4}{5}$ acre of land in Tupelo Township. She wants to sell $\frac{2}{3}$ of her land to her neighbor.

   a. What fraction of an acre does she want to sell? Draw pictures to illustrate your thinking.

   b. Write a number sentence that can be used to solve the problem.

3. Find each answer and explain how you know.

   a. Is $\frac{3}{4} \times 1$ greater than or less than 1?

   b. Is $\frac{3}{4} \times \frac{2}{3}$ greater than or less than 1?

   c. Is $\frac{3}{4} \times \frac{2}{3}$ greater than or less than $\frac{2}{3}$?

   d. Is $\frac{3}{4} \times \frac{2}{3}$ greater than or less than $\frac{3}{4}$?

4. **a.** Use a brownie-pan model to show whether finding $\frac{2}{3}$ of $\frac{3}{4}$ of a pan of brownies means the same thing as finding $\frac{3}{4}$ of $\frac{2}{3}$ of a pan of brownies.

   b. If the brownie pans are the same size, how do the final amounts of brownies compare in the situations in part (a)?

   c. What does this say about $\frac{2}{3} \times \frac{3}{4}$ and $\frac{3}{4} \times \frac{2}{3}$?

5. Find each product. Describe any patterns that you see.

   a. $\frac{1}{2}$ of $\frac{1}{3}$ **b.** $\frac{1}{2}$ of $\frac{1}{4}$ **c.** $\frac{1}{2}$ of $\frac{2}{3}$ **d.** $\frac{1}{2}$ of $\frac{3}{4}$

Notes _____

_____

_____

_____

STUDENT PAGE

6. Mrs. Mace's class is planning a field trip, and $\frac{3}{5}$ of her students want to go to Chicago. Of those who want to go to Chicago, $\frac{2}{3}$ say they want to go to Navy Pier. What fraction of the class wants to go to Navy Pier?

7. Min Ji uses balsa wood to build airplane models. After completing a model, she has a strip of balsa wood measuring $\frac{7}{8}$ yard left over. Shawn wants to buy half of the strip from Min Ji. How long is the strip of wood Shawn wants to buy?

8. Aran has a fruit roll-up for a snack. He gives half of it to Jon. Jon then gives Kiona $\frac{1}{3}$ of his part. How much of the fruit roll-up does each person get?

9. In Vashon's class, three fourths of the students are girls. Four fifths of the girls in Vashon's class have brown hair.

   a. What fraction represents the girls in Vashon's class with brown hair?

   b. How many students do you think are in Vashon's class?

10. Find each product.

   a. $\frac{1}{3}$ of $\frac{2}{3}$ **b.** $\frac{5}{6}$ of 3 **c.** $\frac{2}{3}$ of $\frac{5}{6}$ **d.** $\frac{2}{5}$ of $\frac{5}{8}$

11. Estimate each product. Explain.

   a. $\frac{2}{3} \times 4$ **b.** $2 \times \frac{2}{3}$ **c.** $2\frac{1}{2} \times \frac{2}{3}$

Investigation 3 Multiplying With Fractions **41**

Notes _____

_____

_____

_____

12. Esteban is making turtle brownies. The recipe calls for $\frac{3}{4}$ bag of caramel squares. The bag has 24 caramel squares in it.

   a. How many caramel squares should Esteban use to make one batch of turtle brownies?

   b. Esteban decides to make two batches of turtle brownies. Write a number sentence to show how many bags of caramel squares he will use.

13. Isabel is adding a sun porch onto her house. She measures and finds that covering the entire floor requires 12 rows with $11\frac{1}{3}$ tiles in each row. Write a number sentence to show how many tiles Isabel will use to cover the floor.

14. Judi is making a frame for her little sister's drawing. The wood strip for the frame is 1 inch wide. She allows two extra inches of wood for each corner. If the square is $11\frac{3}{8}$ inches on a side, how much wood should Judi buy?

15. Find each product. Look for patterns to help you.

   a. $\frac{1}{3} \times 18$ **b.** $\frac{2}{3} \times 18$ **c.** $\frac{5}{3} \times 18$ **d.** $1\frac{2}{3} \times 18$

16. Write a number sentence for each situation. (Assume that the fractions are all less than 1.)

   a. a fraction and a whole number with a whole number product

   b. a fraction and a whole number with a product less than 1

   c. a fraction and a whole number with a product greater than 1

   d. a fraction and a whole number with a product between $\frac{1}{2}$ and 1

Homework Help Online
PHSchool.com
For: Help with Exercise 16
Web Code: ame-4316

42   Bits and Pieces II

Notes _____

_____

_____

_____

17. Bonnie and Steve are making snack bags for their daughter's field hockey team. They put $\frac{3}{4}$ cup of pretzels, $\frac{2}{3}$ cup of popcorn, $\frac{1}{3}$ cup of peanuts, and $\frac{1}{4}$ cup of chocolate chips in each bag.

   a. If they want to make 12 bags, how much of each ingredient do they need?

   b. Bonnie decides that she would like to make snack bags for her card club. There are 15 people in the card club. How much of each ingredient will she need?

18. a. When Sierra gets home from school, $\frac{3}{4}$ of a sandwich is left in the refrigerator. She cuts the part remaining into three equal parts and eats two of them. What fraction of the whole sandwich did she eat?

   b. Write a number sentence to show your computation.

19. Mr. Jablonski's class is making fudge for a bake sale. He has a recipe that makes $\frac{3}{4}$ pound of fudge. There are 21 students in the class and each one makes one batch of fudge for the bake sale. How many pounds of fudge do the students make?

20. Carolyn is making cookies. The recipe calls for $1\frac{3}{4}$ cups of brown sugar. If she makes $2\frac{1}{2}$ batches of cookies, how much brown sugar will she need?

For Exercises 21–29, use your algorithm for multiplying fractions to determine each product.

Go Online
PHSchool.com
For: Multiple-Choice Skills Practice
Web Code: ama-4354

21. $\frac{5}{12} \times 1\frac{1}{3}$ **22.** $\frac{2}{7} \times \frac{7}{8}$ **23.** $3\frac{2}{9} \times \frac{7}{3}$

24. $2\frac{2}{5} \times 1\frac{1}{15}$ **25.** $10\frac{3}{4} \times 2\frac{2}{3}$ **26.** $1\frac{1}{8} \times \frac{4}{7}$

27. $\frac{11}{6} \times \frac{9}{10}$ **28.** $\frac{9}{4} \times 1\frac{1}{6}$ **29.** $\frac{5}{2} \times \frac{8}{11}$

Investigation 3 Multiplying With Fractions   **43**

Notes _____

_____

_____

_____

30. **Multiple Choice** Choose the number that, when multiplied by $\frac{4}{7}$, will be greater than $\frac{4}{7}$.

    A. $\frac{1}{7}$　　　　**B.** $\frac{7}{7}$　　　　**C.** $\frac{17}{7}$　　　　**D.** $\frac{4}{7}$

31. **Multiple Choice** Choose the number that, when multiplied by $\frac{4}{7}$, will be less than $\frac{4}{7}$.

    F. $\frac{1}{7}$　　　　**G.** $\frac{7}{7}$　　　　**H.** $\frac{17}{7}$　　　　**J.** $\frac{8}{7}$

32. **Multiple Choice** Choose the number that, when multiplied by $\frac{4}{7}$, will be exactly $\frac{4}{7}$.

    A. $\frac{1}{7}$　　　　**B.** $\frac{7}{7}$　　　　**C.** $\frac{17}{7}$　　　　**D.** $\frac{4}{7}$

33. **a.** How many minutes are in 1 hour?

    b. How many minutes are in $\frac{1}{2}$ hour?

    c. How many minutes are in 0.5 hour?

    d. How many minutes are in 0.1 hour?

    e. How many minutes are in 1.25 hours?

    f. How many hours are in 186 minutes? Express this as a mixed number and as a decimal.

34. A magazine advertises stained glass sun catchers. The ad says that the actual sun catcher is $1\frac{3}{4}$ times the size shown in the picture. Mrs. Inman wants to know how tall the actual sun catcher is. She gets a ruler and measures the sun catcher in the picture. If the sun catcher in the picture is $1\frac{3}{8}$ inches high, how tall is the actual sun catcher?

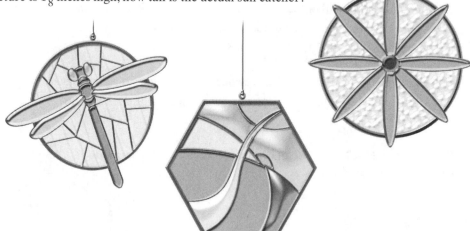

STUDENT PAGE

Notes

35. Violeta and Mandy are making beaded necklaces. They have several beads in various colors and widths. As they design patterns to use, they want to figure out how long the final necklace will be. Violeta and Mandy have the following bead widths to work with.

Widths of Beads

Bead	Width
Trade Neck	$\frac{1}{4}$ inch
Medium Rosebud	$\frac{3}{8}$ inch
Large Rosebud	$\frac{7}{16}$ inch

a. If Mandy uses 30 Trade Neck beads, 6 medium Rosebud beads, and 1 large Rosebud bead, how long will her necklace be?

b. Violeta would like to make a 16-inch necklace by alternating medium and large Rosebud beads. She only has 8 medium Rosebud beads. If she uses 8 medium Rosebud beads and 8 large Rosebud beads, will her necklace be 16 inches long?

Connections

36. Here is a multiplication-division fact family:

$4 \times 5 = 20$ $5 \times 4 = 20$ $20 \div 4 = 5$ $20 \div 5 = 4$

For each number sentence, write a multiplication-division fact family.

a. $3 \times 6 = 18$ **b.** $16 \times 3 = 48$ **c.** $1\frac{1}{2} \times 7 = 10\frac{1}{2}$

d. $15 \div 3 = 5$ **e.** $100 \div 20 = 5$ **f.** $15 \div 1\frac{1}{2} = 10$

37. Roshaun and Lea go to an amusement park. Lea spends $\frac{1}{2}$ of her money, and Roshaun spends $\frac{1}{4}$ of his money. Is it possible for Roshaun to have spent more money than Lea? Explain your reasoning.

38. Bianca and Yoko work together to mow the lawn. Suppose Yoko mows $\frac{5}{12}$ of the lawn and Bianca mows $\frac{2}{5}$ of the lawn. How much lawn still needs to be mowed?

Investigation 3 Multiplying With Fractions   **45**

Notes _____

_____

_____

_____

39. Joe and Ashanti need $2\frac{2}{5}$ bushels of apples to make applesauce. Suppose Joe picks $1\frac{5}{6}$ bushels of apples. How many more bushels need to be picked?

For Exercises 40–45, calculate each sum or difference.

40. $2\frac{2}{3} + 3\frac{5}{6}$

41. $2\frac{8}{10} + 2\frac{4}{5} + 1\frac{1}{2}$

42. $4\frac{3}{10} + 2\frac{2}{6}$

43. $5\frac{5}{8} - 2\frac{2}{3}$

44. $6\frac{7}{10} - 3\frac{4}{5}$

45. $8 - 3\frac{14}{15}$

46. Three students multiply $6 \times \frac{1}{5}$. Their answers are $\frac{6}{5}$, 1.2, and $1\frac{1}{5}$. Match each answer to the strategy described below that is most likely to produce it. Explain.

a. Fala draws six shapes, each representing $\frac{1}{5}$, and fits them together.

b. Bri writes $\frac{6}{1} \times \frac{1}{5}$.

c. Hiroshi writes 6×0.2.

47. Multiple Choice Linda is making bows to put on wreaths. Each bow uses $2\frac{1}{3}$ yards of ribbon. A spool of ribbon contains 15 yards of ribbon. Choose the number of whole bows she can make from one spool.

F. 6   **G.** 7   **H.** 12   **J.** 35

Extensions

48. Find each product.

a. $\frac{2}{3} \times \frac{1}{2} \times \frac{3}{4}$

b. $\frac{5}{8} \times \frac{1}{2} \times \frac{2}{3}$

49. Multiple Choice Choose the best answer for the number of square tiles needed to make a rectangle that is $4\frac{1}{3}$ tiles long by $\frac{1}{2}$ tile wide.

A. $2\frac{1}{3}$ **B.** $2\frac{1}{6}$ **C.** 2   **D.** $2\frac{1}{4}$

Notes _____

_____

_____

_____

Mathematical Reflections 3

In this investigation, you explored situations that required you to multiply fractions. You also developed an algorithm for multiplying fractions. These questions will help you summarize what you have learned.

Think about your answers to these questions. Discuss your ideas with other students and your teacher. Then write a summary of your findings in your notebook.

1. Describe and illustrate your algorithm for multiplying fractions. Explain how you use the algorithm when you multiply fractions by fractions, fractions by mixed numbers, and fractions by whole numbers.

2. When you multiply two whole numbers, neither of which is zero, your answer is always equal to or greater than each of the factors. For example, $3 \times 5 = 15$, and 15 is greater than the factors 3 and 5. Use an example to help explain the following statement.

   When you multiply a fraction less than 1 by another fraction less than 1, your answer is always less than either factor.

3. Explain and illustrate what "of" means when you find a fraction *of* another number. What operation is implied by the word?

Notes _____

_____

_____

_____

Investigation 3

ACE
Assignment Choices

Problem 3.1
Core 1–3, 36, 37
Other *Applications* 4, 5

Problem 3.2
Core 6–8, 10, 38, 39
Other *Applications* 9; unassigned choices from previous problems

Problem 3.3
Core 11–14, 40–45
Other *Applications* 15, *Extensions* 48; unassigned choices from previous problems

Problem 3.4
Core 18–20, 46, 47
Other *Applications* 16, 17; *Extensions* 49; unassigned choices from previous problems

Problem 3.5
Core 21–33
Other *Applications* 34, 35; unassigned choices from previous problems

Adapted For suggestions about adapting Exercise 6 and other ACE problems, see the CMP *Special Needs Handbook*.
Connecting to Prior Units 37: *Bits and Pieces I*

Applications

1. a.

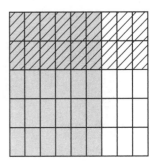

b. $\frac{14}{50} = \frac{7}{25}$

2. a. $\frac{8}{15}$;

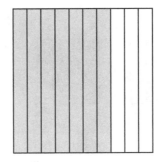
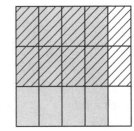

b. $\frac{2}{3} \times \frac{4}{5} = \frac{8}{15}$

3. a. Less than 1; Any number times 1 is itself. $\frac{3}{4}$ times 1 says that you want a $\frac{3}{4}$-part of 1 and $\frac{3}{4}$ of 1 is $\frac{3}{4}$.

b. Less than 1; $\frac{2}{3}$ is less than 1 and multiplying $\frac{3}{4}$ by $\frac{2}{3}$ means that you want $\frac{3}{4}$ of, or part of, $\frac{2}{3}$. Part of $\frac{2}{3}$ will be less than $\frac{2}{3}$ and therefore less than 1.

c. Less than $\frac{2}{3}$; $\frac{3}{4} \times \frac{2}{3}$ means that you want $\frac{3}{4}$ of, or part of, $\frac{2}{3}$. Part of $\frac{2}{3}$ will be less than $\frac{2}{3}$.

d. Less than $\frac{3}{4}$; $\frac{3}{4} \times \frac{2}{3}$ means that you want $\frac{2}{3}$ of, or part of, $\frac{3}{4}$. Part of $\frac{3}{4}$ will be less than $\frac{3}{4}$.

4. a. Possible explanation: Finding $\frac{2}{3}$ of $\frac{3}{4}$ means that you have $\frac{3}{4}$ of a pan of brownies and you are going to take $\frac{2}{3}$ of each of the 3 fourths.

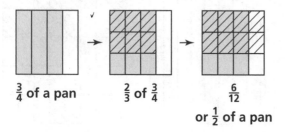

$\frac{3}{4}$ of a pan $\frac{2}{3}$ of $\frac{3}{4}$ $\frac{6}{12}$

or $\frac{1}{2}$ of a pan

Finding $\frac{3}{4}$ of $\frac{2}{3}$ means that you start with a pan of brownies that is $\frac{2}{3}$ full. You are going to take $\frac{3}{4}$ of each of the 2 thirds.

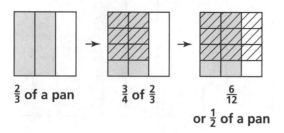

$\frac{2}{3}$ of a pan $\frac{3}{4}$ of $\frac{2}{3}$ $\frac{6}{12}$

or $\frac{1}{2}$ of a pan

b. Possible explanation: With either problem you get $\frac{1}{2}$ of a pan of brownies.

c. Possible explanation: The answer to both multiplication problems is the same, but how you find that answer is different in each problem when you show it with a brownie pan model. In one you are taking $\frac{2}{3}$ of something, and in the other you are taking $\frac{3}{4}$ of something.

5. a. $\frac{1}{2}$ of $\frac{1}{3} = \frac{1}{6}$ **b.** $\frac{1}{2}$ of $\frac{1}{4} = \frac{1}{8}$
  c. $\frac{1}{2}$ of $\frac{2}{3} = \frac{2}{6}$, or $\frac{1}{3}$ **d.** $\frac{1}{2}$ of $\frac{3}{4} = \frac{3}{8}$
When you take half of a fraction, the denominator doubles. This happens because if you have thirds (e.g. a thirds fraction strip) and you fold each third in half, it makes twice as many pieces because they are half the size of the original third.

6. $\frac{2}{3} \times \frac{3}{5} = \frac{2}{5}$ of the class wants to go to Navy Pier.

7. $\frac{1}{2}$ of $\frac{7}{8} = \frac{7}{16}$ yard

8. Aran: $\frac{1}{2}$
  Jon: $\frac{2}{3}$ of $\frac{1}{2} = \frac{2}{6}$, or $\frac{1}{3}$
  Kiona: $\frac{1}{3}$ of $\frac{1}{2} = \frac{1}{6}$

9. a. $\frac{4}{5} \times \frac{3}{4} = \frac{3}{5}$ have brown hair.
  b. Answers will vary: Any multiple of 20 is possible.

10. a. $\frac{2}{9}$ **b.** $\frac{15}{6} = 2\frac{3}{6} = 2\frac{1}{2}$
  c. $\frac{10}{18} = \frac{5}{9}$ **d.** $\frac{10}{40} = \frac{1}{4}$

11. a. Possible answer: almost 3; $\frac{2}{3}$ is a little more than $\frac{1}{2}$. If you had 4 halves, you would get 2, but since it is a little more times 4, you get almost 3.

  b. Possible answer: about $1\frac{1}{4}$; $\frac{2}{3}$ is between $\frac{1}{2}$ and $\frac{3}{4}$. If you double $\frac{1}{2}$, you get 1, and if you double $\frac{3}{4}$, you get $1\frac{1}{2}$. Doubling $\frac{2}{3}$ will be between 1 and $1\frac{1}{2}$ at about $1\frac{1}{4}$.

  c. Possible answer: about $1\frac{1}{2}$; if $\frac{2}{3} \times 2$ is about $1\frac{1}{4}$ [see part (b)], then $2\frac{1}{2} \times \frac{2}{3}$ is a little more, or about $1\frac{1}{2}$.

12. a. 18 caramel squares
  b. $\frac{3}{4} \times 2 = 1\frac{1}{2}$ bags will be used.

13. $12 \times 11\frac{1}{3} = 136$ tiles

14. $11\frac{3}{8} \times 4 + 2 \times 4 = 53\frac{1}{2}$ in.

15. a. $\frac{1}{3} \times 18 = 6$　　**b.** $\frac{2}{3} \times 18 = 12$

　　c. $\frac{5}{3} \times 18 = 30$　　**d.** $1\frac{2}{3} \times 18 = 30$

16. a. Possible answers: $\frac{3}{4} \times 4 = 3$ or $\frac{5}{8} \times 8 = 5$

　　b. Possible answers: $\frac{9}{10} \times 1 = \frac{9}{10}$ or $\frac{2}{9} \times 2 = \frac{4}{9}$

　　c. Possible answers: $\frac{5}{6} \times 2 = \frac{10}{6}$ or $\frac{3}{8} \times 5 = \frac{15}{8}$

　　d. Possible answers: $\frac{3}{8} \times 2 = \frac{6}{8}$ or $\frac{1}{15} \times 9 = \frac{9}{15}$

17. a. $\frac{3}{4} \times 12 = 9$ cups of pretzels, $\frac{2}{3} \times 12 = 8$ cups of popcorn, $\frac{1}{3}$ of $12 = 4$ cups of peanuts, $\frac{1}{4} \times 12 = 3$ cups chocolate chips

　　b. $\frac{3}{4} \times 15 = \frac{45}{4} = 11\frac{1}{4}$ cups of pretzels,

　　$\frac{2}{3} \times 15 = \frac{30}{3} = 10$ cups of popcorn,

　　$\frac{1}{3} \times 15 = 5$ cups of peanuts,

　　$\frac{1}{4} \times 15 = \frac{15}{4} = 3\frac{3}{4}$ cups of chocolate chips

18. a. $\frac{1}{2}$ of the whole sandwich

　　b. $\frac{2}{3} \times \frac{3}{4} = \frac{1}{2}$

19. $\frac{3}{4} \times 21 = 15\frac{3}{4}$ lbs.　**20.** $1\frac{3}{4} \times 2\frac{1}{2} = 4\frac{3}{8}$ cups

21. $\frac{20}{36} = \frac{10}{18} = \frac{5}{9}$　　　**22.** $\frac{14}{56} = \frac{2}{8} = \frac{1}{4}$

23. $\frac{203}{27} = 7\frac{14}{27}$　　　**24.** $\frac{192}{75} = 2\frac{42}{75} = 2\frac{14}{25}$

25. $\frac{344}{12} = 28\frac{8}{12} = 28\frac{2}{3}$　　**26.** $\frac{36}{56} = \frac{18}{28} = \frac{9}{14}$

27. $\frac{99}{60} = 1\frac{39}{60} = 1\frac{13}{20}$　　**28.** $\frac{63}{24} = 2\frac{15}{24} = 2\frac{5}{8}$

29. $\frac{40}{22} = 1\frac{18}{22} = 1\frac{9}{11}$　　**30.** C

31. F　　　　　　**32.** B

33. a. 60 mins **b.** 30 mins　**c.** 30 mins

　　d. 6 mins　**e.** 75 mins　**f.** $3\frac{1}{10}$ or 3.1 hours

34. $2\frac{13}{32}$ inches

35. a. $10\frac{3}{16}$ inches

　　b. No. Since each bead is less than 1 inch, the 16 beads cannot total 16 inches.

Connections

36. a. $3 \times 6 = 18, 6 \times 3 = 18, 18 \div 3 = 6,$ and $18 \div 6 = 3$

　　b. $16 \times 3 = 48, 3 \times 16 = 48, 48 \div 3 = 16,$ and $48 \div 16 = 3$

　　c. $1\frac{1}{2} \times 7 = 10\frac{1}{2}, 7 \times 1\frac{1}{2} = 10\frac{1}{2},$ $10\frac{1}{2} \div 7 = 1\frac{1}{2},$ and $10\frac{1}{2} \div 1\frac{1}{2} = 7$

　　d. $15 \div 3 = 5, 15 \div 5 = 3, 3 \times 5 = 15,$ and $5 \times 3 = 15$

　　e. $100 \div 20 = 5, 100 \div 5 = 20, 5 \times 20 = 100,$ and $20 \times 5 = 100$

　　f. $15 \div 1\frac{1}{2} = 10, 15 \div 10 = 1\frac{1}{2}, 1\frac{1}{2} \times 10 = 15,$ and $10 \times 1\frac{1}{2} = 15$

37. Yes, it is possible. Possible explanation: Suppose Lea had $4 and Roshaun had $20. Then Lea would have spent half of $4, or $2, and Roshaun would have spent $\frac{1}{4}$ of $20, or $5. Thus, Roshaun would have spent more than Lea.

38. $\frac{11}{60}$ of the lawn still needs to be mowed.

39. $\frac{17}{30}$ bushel of apples

40. $6\frac{1}{2}$　　**41.** $7\frac{1}{10}$　　**42.** $6\frac{19}{30}$　　**43.** $2\frac{23}{24}$

44. $2\frac{9}{10}$　　**45.** $4\frac{1}{15}$

46. a. $1\frac{1}{5}$; Fala is fitting together six $\frac{1}{5}$-pie shapes. When she fits them together, five will make one whole and there will be one fifth left. Her approach will lead to the solution $1\frac{1}{5}$.

　　b. $\frac{6}{5}$; If Bri multiplies the numerators and multiplies the denominators, she gets $\frac{6}{5}$.

　　c. 1.2; Hiroshi is using decimals to solve the same problem, so he is most likely to get a decimal answer.

47. F

Extensions

48. a. $\frac{1}{4}$ **b.** $\frac{5}{24}$

49. B

Possible Answers to Mathematical Reflections

1. To multiply a fraction by a fraction, you multiply the numerators of each fraction to get the numerator of the product and multiply the denominators of each fraction to get the denominator of the product. If the problem has mixed numbers or whole numbers, change them into fractions. Then multiply using the same method for multiplying a fraction by a fraction.

2. When you multiply a fraction by a fraction, you are taking a part of a part of something. You can use the problem $\frac{1}{4} \times \frac{1}{2}$ and brownie pans to think about this. You have half of a brownie pan, and then you take one-fourth of the half of a pan. This will give you a part of the half, one-eighth, which means the product is less than either of the factors.

3. When you take a fraction of another number, you are taking a part of that number. This implies that you are multiplying. Unlike multiplying with whole numbers where you make some number of whole groups of some amount, you are taking a part of some amount such as half "of" one-fourth.

Investigation 4 Dividing With Fractions

Mathematical and Problem-Solving Goals

- Use models to represent division situations (a whole number divided by a fraction, a fraction divided by a whole number, and a fraction divided by a fraction)

- Develop and use strategies for dividing a whole number by a fraction, a fraction by a whole number, and a fraction by a fraction

- Understand when division is the appropriate operation

- Develop an efficient algorithm to solve any fraction division problem

- Explore the inverse operations of multiplication and division

Summary of Problems

Problem 4.1 Preparing Food

Students divide whole numbers by fractions to decide how many pizzas can be made with given amounts of cheese.

Problem 4.2 Fundraising Continues

Students divide fractions by whole numbers to determine shares.

Problem 4.3 Summer Work

Students divide to find the number of bows that can be made with given amounts of ribbon.

Problem 4.4 Writing a Division Algorithm

Students develop an efficient algorithm for division.

Mathematics Background

For background on fraction division, see pages 9–11.

	Suggested Pacing	Materials for Students	Materials for Teachers	ACE Assignments
All	$5\frac{1}{2}$ days	Calculators, student notebooks	Blank transparencies and transparency markers	
4.1	$1\frac{1}{2}$ days	Blank transparencies and transparency markers	Transparency 4.1	1–4, 24–29
4.2	1 day			5–10, 30–35, 41
4.3	1 day			11–14, 36, 37
4.4	$1\frac{1}{2}$ days	Large chart paper or blank transparencies, markers	Transparency 4.4	15–23, 38–40
MR	$\frac{1}{2}$ day			

5-14
30-37, 41

Introducing the Investigation: When Is Division Appropriate?

It is important to use what students know about whole number division to help stimulate their thinking about division situations that involve fractions. To review their experiences with whole numbers and division, we begin the investigation with a Getting Ready. Students explore whole number division situations in order to understand when division is an appropriate operation.

Begin by introducing the investigation.

- *In this investigation you are going to explore division of fractions. Before we look at fractions let's look at division with whole numbers. Working with a partner, use words, pictures, or other ways to explain why 12 ÷ 4 = 3.*

As students look for examples of different ways to explain, they have to think about meanings of division. Have students record their ideas on a transparency.

Division situations can often be categorized as one of two types of problems—sharing problems (also called partitive division) or grouping problems (also called measurement division). Students will generally show both ways of thinking. In the class discussion, focus on how you recognize when division is an appropriate operation to use and how the answer should be interpreted in the given situation. Have students share their ideas. Talk about what each number represents in the contexts that students use.

Possible Approach: Sharing

In Figure 1, the student has arranged 12 candy bars in a row and distributed them one by one to the circles representing the four friends. This is like dealing out the candy bars one by one among the four friends until they are all gone.

Suggested Questions When students describe this approach ask questions such as:

- *How did you decide that four people can get three candy bars?* (I gave each of the four people one candy bar at a time until they were gone.)

- *In your problem what does the 4 tell you?* (The 4 tells you how many people received three candy bars.)

- *In your problem what does the 3 tell you?* (The 3 tells how many candy bars each person gets.)

Possible Approach: Grouping

We have 12 candy bars. I am going to give each person 4 candy bars until they are all gone. 12 (bars) − 4 (a group for one person) = 8 (bars left). 8 − 4 = 4 and finally, 4 − 4 = 0. We subtracted three groups of four so I can share the candy bars with three people.

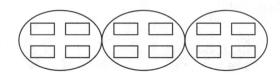

Figure 1

Candy Bars

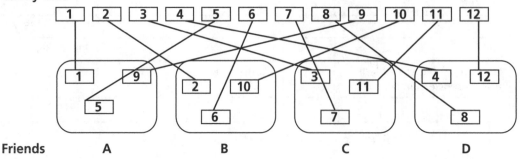

Friends   A   B   C   D

Suggested Questions When students describe this approach ask questions such as:

- *How did you decide that three people can get four candy bars?* (I gave each person four candy bars until they were gone.)

- *In your problem what does the 4 tell you?* (The 4 tells you how candy bars in a group for each person.)

- *In your problem what does the 3 tell you?* (The 3 tells how many people you can give candy bars to.)

Move the conversation toward distinguishing between grouping and sharing situations.

- *Can you describe the difference between these two types of situations?* (In a grouping situation the 4 is how many are in a group and the 3 is how many groups. In the sharing situation the 4 is how many people will share and the 3 is what each one will get.)

- *So grouping problems look like this:*

$$12 \div 4 = 3$$

number in   how many
each group   groups

- *Sharing problems look like this:*

$$12 \div 4 = 3$$

share among   how much
4 people   each one gets

In order to do the Getting Ready, students will need to see the difference between the two situations. Once you have distinguished between the two division situations, you may want to have half of the students in pairs write a grouping division problem and the other half write a sharing division problem. Display a few of their problems and talk about which type of division problem it is. When you feel students are relatively comfortable with the two models, introduce the Getting Ready. Have students decide if each situation is a sharing or grouping situation.

The first and third examples are sharing problems. You are sharing the swimming and selling. The labeled division sentences will look like this:

$$120 \div 24 = 5$$

# of miles   # of   # of miles
to be shared ÷ swimmers = per swimmer

$$600 \div 20 = 30$$

# of boxes   # of boxes
to sell   ÷ # of sellers   = per seller
        (band   (band
        members)   member)

The second example is a grouping problem. Note the difference in how this problem is labeled. Here you are finding the number of buses needed. You are *not* finding the share per bus. The share (or group size) is given in the problem as 30 students per bus.

$$360 \div 30 = 12$$

# of students ÷   # of students   # of
        per bus   = buses

With the class, notice the types of quantities in the problems. Even though these are whole numbers and represent counts of things, these kinds of questions are setting the stage for the more complicated work with fractions.

Suggested Questions

- *What kind of numbers (quantities) are given or implied in the problem?*

- *What do you need to know?*

- *What will your answer tell us?*

To summarize, in a sharing situation you know the *amount* to be shared and the *number of entities* that will receive a share. The answer to the division, the quotient, is the *amount per share*. In problems that call for grouping, what is known is the *total quantity* and the *amount per group*. The quotient is the *number of groups* of the given size that can be made from the quantity given.

Goals

- Use models to represent a whole number divided by a fraction

- Develop and use strategies for dividing a whole number by a fraction

- Understand when division is an appropriate operation

Question A uses situations that involve division by a unit fraction. Understanding what happens in cases where whole numbers are divided by unit fractions provides a foundation on which division by non-unit fractions can be built. Question B asks students to extend what they have learned about division with unit fractions to make sense of situations with non-unit fractions.

Mathematics Background

For background on division and inverse relationships, see pages 9–12.

Launch 4.1

Suggested Questions Use the introduction to Problem 4.1 in the student edition to shift the focus from whole number to fraction situations.

- *When you do the division* 12 ÷ 5, *what does the answer mean?* (How many fives are in 12 wholes.)

- *Five does not go into 12 an even, or whole, number of times. Can we use a fraction to show how many times 5 goes into 12?*

  $(12 \div 5 = 2\frac{2}{5})$

- *What does the fraction part of the answer mean?* (We are making groups of five. We can make two whole groups and $\frac{2}{5}$ of another group.)

- *How would you write a division problem for "How many $\frac{3}{4}$'s are in 14?"* $(14 \div \frac{3}{4})$

- *We are going to work on problems like this in Problem 4.1. Before we start though, what is a reasonable estimate for how many times $\frac{3}{4}$ will go into 14? Remember that you know that*

14 ÷ 1 = 14. (If you can make 14 groups of 1, you should be able to make at least 14 groups of $\frac{3}{4}$ since they are smaller groups. Maybe 16 or even 20 would be reasonable.)

- *Parts of Problem 4.1 involve fractions. Use what you know about whole number computation and about fractions to find ways to answer these questions.*

- *Let's do a Think-Pair-Share. Work alone for five minutes. Then pair with your partner and share what you have done so far. Work together until I call you back to share with the whole class. Be sure that you remember that drawing a picture is a good way to help yourself think through each situation. When everyone gets though A and B, I am going to stop you and we will summarize those questions.*

If you think your class will be pressed for time, assign Questions C–F for homework. Complete the summary of the problem the next day.

Explore 4.1

As the class works, circulate paying attention to how students are thinking about the problems and where they are having difficulty. Encourage the students to draw pictures or diagrams to model the problems. Also, encourage the students to write number sentences that represent their pictures and reflect how they solved the problem. Ask questions about whether the problems seem to be about sharing something equally or about how many groups or things of a certain kind can be made.

You might want to have students who used diagrams for the various problems put them on a transparency so you can display them in the summary.

Summarize 4.1

Begin the summary by asking students if the pizza problems are grouping or sharing problems. The problems used are examples of grouping problems. In each case you know how much cheese you have and how much is needed for each group (pizza). You do not know how many groups (pizzas) you can make.

As you go over the parts of Question A, have any students who drew diagrams share their drawings.

The problems are easy once the students draw diagrams and use explanations such as the following:

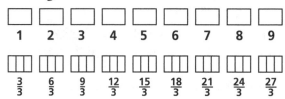

The student who drew the above diagram said, "I have 9 bars of cheese. Since each bar has 3 thirds, I can multiply 9×3 to find how many thirds in 9. So 27 pizzas can be made with 9 bars of cheese when each pizza takes $\frac{1}{3}$ cup of cheese."

Suggested Questions Ask questions like the following:

- *What number sentence represents how many $\frac{1}{3}$'s are in 9?* ($9 \div \frac{1}{3} = 27$)

- *Your solution sounds like you used the number sentence $9 \times 3 = 27$. Do you agree?* (Yes. Since each cup has 3 thirds, I can find how many pizzas can be made by multiplying 9 by 3.)

Throughout the discussion of the parts of Question A continue to attach notation to students' reasoning. Students who use common denominators may reason like this: $9 \div \frac{1}{3}$ is the same as $\frac{27}{3} \div \frac{1}{3}$. This means how many thirds are in 27 thirds.

- *How would you represent this approach?* ($\frac{27}{3} \div \frac{1}{3} = 27$)

- *What does the $\frac{27}{3}$ represent?* (9 wholes)

- *What does the division problem $\frac{27}{3}$ divided by $\frac{1}{3}$ ask?* (How many $\frac{1}{3}$'s are in 27 thirds.)

- *Why did the 9 get rewritten as $\frac{27}{3}$?* (So you can think about the division problem as 27 thirds and try to find out how many $\frac{1}{3}$'s are in $\frac{27}{3}$.)

- *What could a diagram for this approach look like?* (It could look like the diagram used earlier to represent $9 \div \frac{1}{3}$. The second row of the diagram shows the 9 wholes as $\frac{27}{3}$.)

As you move through the summary for Question A, be sure both of these approaches arise. You will need to suggest an approach if it does not come up.

- *Your drawings and explanations show that there are two number sentences that make sense for problems like $9 \div \frac{1}{3}$.*

$$9 \times 3 = 27$$

$$\frac{27}{3} \div \frac{1}{3} = 27$$

Once these two ideas and their notation are brought out, and students seem to have a good grasp of what is happening in each situation, move the conversation to Question B. As you discuss each of the parts of Question B, ask questions that help students to generalize a strategy for dividing a whole number by a unit fraction and dividing a whole number by a non-unit fraction. Students may need help writing number sentences that model their explanations.

- *In Question B, we want to use what you know about dividing whole numbers with unit fractions to make sense of problems where the numerator of the divisor is greater than 1. For example, how can we use what we did to solve $9 \div \frac{1}{3}$ to solve the problem $9 \div \frac{2}{3}$ and the other problems?*

Have a group share their diagram for $9 \div \frac{2}{3}$. The diagram will look different because it takes 2 of the 3 thirds to make one of the desired groups.

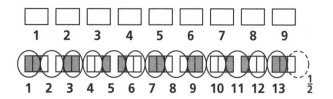

- *What are you trying to find out in the problem $9 \div \frac{2}{3}$?* (How many $\frac{2}{3}$'s are in 9 wholes.)

- *Where did the 13 and the $\frac{1}{2}$ come from?* (There are 13 complete $\frac{2}{3}$'s and half of a $\frac{2}{3}$ in 9. After doing as many sets of $\frac{2}{3}$ as possible there was $\frac{1}{3}$ left. $\frac{1}{3}$ is half of $\frac{2}{3}$. So there are $13\frac{1}{2}$ $\frac{2}{3}$'s in 9 wholes.)

- *How does this problem compare to $9 \div \frac{1}{3}$?* (You still divide each rectangle into thirds. But, groups of $\frac{2}{3}$ are twice as big as groups of $\frac{1}{3}$. Since they are twice as big you get half as many. That is why you get $13\frac{1}{2}$. It is half of 27 or $27 \div 2$.)

- *So you are saying that you can use the answer from $9 \div \frac{1}{3}$ to find the answer to $9 \div \frac{2}{3}$. When we did $9 \div \frac{1}{3}$ in Question A we wrote that $9 \div \frac{1}{3} = 9 \times 3$. What would we write as a number sentence for $9 \div \frac{2}{3}$* (To find $9 \div \frac{2}{3}$ you would take $9 \times 3 \div 2 = 13\frac{1}{2}$ groups of $\frac{2}{3}$.)

- *Why are you dividing by 2?* (It takes $\frac{2}{3}$ of a bar to make a pizza. Since each bar has 3 thirds in it, we can multiply 9×3 to find out how many thirds are in 9 wholes. Since it takes 2 of the thirds for each pizza, we need to divide by 2.)

- *Let's look at the other two cases, $\frac{3}{3}$ and $\frac{4}{3}$, and see if the same reasoning works.*

Work on writing out number sentences for each of the cases for thirds.

- *So, explain how you can divide any whole number by a fraction.* (Multiply by the denominator and divide by the numerator of the divisor.)

Also discuss the common denominator approach.

- *Did anyone try using common denominators like we did when we rewrote $9 \div \frac{1}{3}$ as $\frac{27}{3} \div \frac{1}{3}$?*

- *How would you use a diagram to show $\frac{27}{3} \div \frac{2}{3}$?* (You can use the same diagram as you used for the multiply-by-denominator-and-divide-by-numerator approach.)

- *Why does this approach work?* (You are rewriting 9 as $\frac{27}{3}$. $\frac{27}{3}$ is the number of thirds in 9 wholes. When you divide by $\frac{2}{3}$, it means that each pizza uses $\frac{2}{3}$ of a bar of cheese and you are finding how many sets of 2 thirds are in 27 thirds.)

- *Try this approach on several problems to be sure it works.*

Question C provides a place for students to use the approaches developed in A and B and for you to informally assess students' progress. Question D explicitly asks students to express the relationship between dividing a whole number by $\frac{1}{3}$ to dividing the same number by $\frac{2}{3}$.

- *Why is the answer to $8 \div \frac{2}{3}$ exactly half of the answer to $8 \div \frac{1}{3}$? While they may offer different wording to explain, the crucial idea is that it takes two of the one-third pieces to make a two-thirds piece.*

Some students may see that you multiply by the reciprocal. Others may feel more comfortable with saying that you multiply the dividend by the denominator of the divisor and then divide the product by the numerator of the divisor. Still others may prefer to make common denominators and then divide the numerators.

In Question E, discuss student strategies. Ask students to justify their answers and share any drawings they did to make sense of the problem. Have students exchange the problems they created with another pair of students and give them time to work each other's problems. Then have the writers of some of the problems show his or her drawings and explain what type the problem is: sharing or grouping. Discuss with the class whether they agree with the writer.

Check for Understanding

Naylah has nine bars of cheese. How many pizzas can Naylah make if each takes $\frac{1}{5}$ bar of cheese? (45) If each takes $\frac{2}{5}$ bar of cheese? ($22\frac{1}{2}$) If each takes $\frac{3}{5}$ bar of cheese? (15) If each takes $\frac{4}{5}$ bar of cheese? ($11\frac{1}{4}$) If each takes $\frac{5}{5}$ bar of cheese? (9) If each takes $\frac{6}{5}$ bar of cheese? ($7\frac{1}{2}$)

4.1 Preparing Food

Mathematical Goals

- Use models to represent a whole number divided by a fraction
- Develop and use strategies for dividing a whole number by a fraction
- Understand when division is an appropriate operation

Launch

Begin by introducing the investigation.

- *In this investigation, you are going to explore division of fractions. Before we look at fractions let's look at division with whole numbers. Working with a partner, use words, pictures, or other ways to explain why* $12 \div 4 = 3$.

Have students record their ideas on a transparency. Focus the discussion on how you recognize when division is an appropriate operation and how to interpret the quotient. Using the students' work, introduce the two major types of division problems and the language of "sharing" and "grouping." In order to do the Getting Ready, students will need to see the difference between the two situations. Please read the extended Teacher's Guide for a detailed discussion of sharing, grouping, and the Getting Ready.

Introduce Problem 4.1.

- *When you do* $12 \div 5$, *what does the answer mean?*
- *Five does not go into 12 an even, or whole, number of times. Can we use a fraction to show how many times 5 goes into 12?*
- *How would you write a division problem for "How many* $\frac{3}{4}$*'s are in 14?"*
- *What is a reasonable estimate for* $14 \div \frac{3}{4}$*?*
- *With Problem 4.1, use what you know about whole number computation and fractions to find ways to answer these questions.*

Read through Problem 4.1 with students. Use a Think-Pair-Share.

Materials
- Transparency 4.1

Vocabulary
- grouping
- sharing

Explore

Look for how students are thinking about the problems and where they are having difficulty. Encourage the use of diagrams and number sentences.

Materials
- Blank transparencies
- Markers

Summarize

Ask students to share strategies and diagrams for Question A. Look for reasoning like: "I have 9 bars of cheese. Each bar has 3 thirds, so I can multiply 9×3 to find how many thirds are in 9." Look for a common denominator approach: "$9 \div \frac{1}{3}$ is the same as $\frac{27}{3} \div \frac{1}{3}$. How many $\frac{1}{3}$'s are in 27 thirds. There are 3 thirds in 1 whole, so 3×9 (wholes) is 27." If these

Materials
- Student notebooks

continued on next page

approaches do not come out, suggest them. Attach number sentences to reasoning.

$$9 \div \tfrac{1}{3} \rightarrow 9 \times 3 = 27 \quad \text{or} \quad 9 \div \tfrac{1}{3} \rightarrow \tfrac{27}{3} \div \tfrac{1}{3} = 27$$

In Question B, compare diagrams for related problems such as $9 \div \tfrac{1}{3}$ and $9 \div \tfrac{2}{3}$. Some will use a common denominator approach. Others will build on the 3×9 approach used with $9 \div \tfrac{1}{3}$. "Since you are making groups of 2 thirds, rather than 1 third, $9 \div \tfrac{2}{3}$ will be half of $9 \div \tfrac{1}{3}$ or $9 \times 3 \div 2 = 13\tfrac{1}{2}$.

ACE Assignment Guide for Problem 4.1

Core 1, 2, 24–29
Other *Applications* 3, 4

Adapted For suggestions about adapting Exercise 1 and other ACE exercises, see the CMP *Special Needs Handbook*.

Answers to Problem 4.1

See text of the Summarize for supporting drawings.

A. 1. $9 \div \tfrac{1}{3} = 27$ pizzas

   2. $9 \div \tfrac{1}{4} = 36$ pizzas

   3. $9 \div \tfrac{1}{5} = 45$ pizzas

   4. $9 \div \tfrac{1}{6} = 54$ pizzas

   5. $9 \div \tfrac{1}{7} = 63$ pizzas

   6. $9 \div \tfrac{1}{8} = 72$ pizzas

B. 1. $9 \div \tfrac{1}{3} = 27$ pizzas

   2. $9 \div \tfrac{2}{3} = 13\tfrac{1}{2}$ pizzas

   3. $9 \div \tfrac{3}{3} = 9$ pizzas

   4. $9 \div \tfrac{4}{3} = 6\tfrac{3}{4}$ pizzas

   5. $13\tfrac{1}{2}$ means that Frank has enough cheese to make 13 whole pizzas and $\tfrac{1}{2}$ of a pizza.

C. 1. $12 \div \tfrac{1}{3} = 36$

2. $12 \div \tfrac{2}{3} = 18$

3. $12 \div \tfrac{5}{3} = 7\tfrac{1}{5}$

4. $12 \div \tfrac{1}{6} = 72$

5. $12 \div \tfrac{5}{6} = 14\tfrac{2}{5}$

6. $12 \div \tfrac{7}{6} = 10\tfrac{2}{7}$

7. There is enough cheese to make 7 full pizzas and one-fifth of another.

D. 1. Possible answer: There are 3 thirds in each whole, so there are 8×3 thirds in 8. This gives 24. Since $8 \div \tfrac{2}{3}$ asks how many two-thirds there are in 8, we know there will be half as many as the number of one-thirds, so the answer will be half the answer to $8 \div \tfrac{1}{3}$, or 12.

   2. Possible answer: It's exactly half because $\tfrac{2}{3}$ has twice as many thirds as $\tfrac{1}{3}$, so $\tfrac{2}{3}$ will go into 8 half as many times as $\tfrac{1}{3}$.

E. Possible answer: Divide the whole number by the numerator of the fraction, then multiply by the denominator of the fraction.

F. Answers may vary. Possible answer: Sam has 12 cups of milk. He is making individual custards that take $\tfrac{2}{3}$ of a cup of milk each. How many can he make? To solve the problem we need to find out how many two-thirds there are in 12. To do this we need to divide 12 by $\tfrac{2}{3}$.

Goals

- Use models to represent a fraction divided by a whole number

- Develop and use strategies for dividing a fraction by a whole number

- Understand when division is an appropriate operation

We have organized the problems to help students build on their ideas from Problem 4.1 to see a pattern that will lead to an algorithm. Problem 4.2 has five questions, two of which give a different situation with several parts. In Question A, all the problems are of the unit fraction divided by a whole number form. In Question B, the parts all involve dividing a non-unit fraction by a whole number. Questions C–E are essential. Here the work is done to relate the students' experiences with an algorithm. Here also, the students firm up their understanding by actually writing problems that fit the computation $\frac{8}{3} \div 4$.

Launch 4.2

Suggested Questions

- *Who can tell me how to change $\frac{3}{5}$ into a decimal?* (Divide the 5 into the 3.)

- *Why does that make sense?* (Because $\frac{3}{5}$ means $3 \div 5$.)

- *So a fraction can be thought of as another way to show division. This means that $\frac{2}{3}$ can be thought of as $2 \div 3$. If you divide 2 by 3, you get $\frac{2}{3}$.*

- *Now give me a situation in which $2 \div 3$ would be an appropriate interpretation of a fraction.* (Three people order two pizzas to share equally. How much does each get? The answer can be obtained by computing $2 \div 3$, which gives $\frac{2}{3}$. Another situation is when you want to convert a fraction to a decimal. Dividing 2 by 3 with or without a calculator gives you the decimal approximation for $\frac{2}{3}$.)

- *In Investigation 3 we looked at products of two numbers that give exactly 1 as the answer. Some examples are $\frac{1}{2} \times 2 = 1$; $3 \times \frac{1}{3} = 1$; $\frac{2}{3} \times \frac{3}{2} = 1$. What did we call these pairs of numbers whose product is exactly 1?* (We called them reciprocals.)

- *What is the reciprocal of $\frac{3}{5}$? ($\frac{5}{3}$) Of 7? ($\frac{1}{7}$)*

- *How about a mixed number such as $4\frac{1}{3}$? What is its reciprocal?* (First we have to write $4\frac{1}{3}$ as a fraction. This would be $\frac{13}{3}$. This means that the reciprocal is $\frac{3}{13}$ because $\frac{13}{3} \times \frac{3}{13} = 1$)

- *Today we have a problem about peanuts to solve. As we read it, pay attention to what is different than the kinds of problems in Problem 4.1.*

Read Question A with your students and remind them of things like the following:

- *Remember that drawing a diagram is often very helpful.*

- *Remember to label your answer so that we know what that number you get is telling us about the situation.*

- *What are the numbers (quantities) given in the problem? Remember to label each so you know what the number means.*

- *What do you need to find?*

- *What does the answer tell you?*

Have the students work on Questions A and B individually and then in pairs to compare solutions and strategies. If you think you will be pressed for time, you can assign any of Questions C–E for homework and discuss them the next day.

Explore 4.2

As students work, walk around and ask questions to make sure that they notice the types of problems that make up Questions A and B. Ask a group to make up another problem that fits the kind of problem called for in Questions A or B.

INVESTIGATION 4

Suggested Question Push them to think about short cuts.

- *Do you see a pattern that would give you a short way of finding the answer?*

You may need to help students share their ideas and drawings for these problems. The drawings are related to those done earlier, but now we are working with a fractional part of something and we need to share it equally among a whole number of entities or people. Ask students what kinds of problems these are—grouping or sharing.

Summarize 4.2

Review the work of Questions A and B with the students. Call on students to illustrate how they did the divisions called for in Questions A and B.

Suggested Question

- *Who can give me an answer for Question A, part (1), and explain why you think you are correct?*

Some students may draw diagrams and provide explanations like the following. With this type of diagram you can make a connection to the brownie pans or area models and multiplication of fractions in Investigation 3.

Student One:

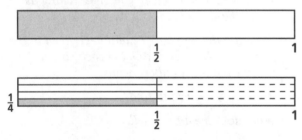

The student who drew the above diagram said, "I drew a fraction strip to show $\frac{1}{2}$. Then I needed to divide this amount into four parts. This lets me find $\frac{1}{4}$ of the amount because that is what each will get. Then I had to name the small part that shows $\frac{1}{4}$ of $\frac{1}{2}$. The picture shows that $\frac{1}{4} \times \frac{1}{2} = \frac{1}{8}$ since we have eight equal parts in the whole. So each person gets $\frac{1}{8}$ pound of peanuts."

Capitalize on this response to point out that the problem called for the computation $\frac{1}{2} \div 4$ and this diagram shows that $\frac{1}{2} \div 4$ is the same as $\frac{1}{2} \times \frac{1}{4}$ which is $\frac{1}{8}$.

Suggested Questions

- *This diagram reminds me of the brownie pan problems you did in Investigation 3. What multiplication problem would this model represent?* ($\frac{1}{2} \times \frac{1}{4} = \frac{1}{8}$).

- *Why does it make sense that $\frac{1}{2} \div 4$ is the same as $\frac{1}{2} \times \frac{1}{4}$ which is $\frac{1}{8}$?* (Dividing something into four parts is the same as taking $\frac{1}{4}$ of that thing.)

Some students will draw a diagram for $\frac{1}{2} \div 4$ that looks like this one:

Student Two:

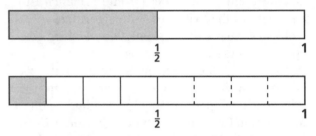

The student who drew this diagram said, "I first made a drawing of $\frac{1}{2}$. Then I divided $\frac{1}{2}$ into four parts because there are four people to share. Now I can see that each person gets $\frac{1}{8}$ of a pound of peanuts. So $\frac{1}{2} \div 4 = \frac{1}{8}$. This makes sense because you will have smaller pieces than the original $\frac{1}{2}$ and they will be four times smaller or $\frac{1}{4}$ as large. I guess we could do this by seeing that $\frac{1}{2} \div 4 = \frac{1}{2} \times \frac{1}{4} = \frac{1}{8}$."

Each of these diagrams helps students move from the division problem to multiplying by the reciprocal. Continue with the rest of the parts of Question A. Look at other approaches that students took to make sense of the problems.

Suggested Questions Move on to Question B in which the fractional parts given are not unit fractions.

- *Who can tell me how these problems in Question B are different from those in Question A?* (They have non-unit fraction parts to be shared.)

- *Who can tell me how they thought about Question B, part (1)?* (I thought about the problem just like the ones in Question A. First I worked it for $\frac{1}{4}$ of a bar and then multiplied my answer by 3. Here were my steps: $\frac{1}{4} \div 2 = \frac{1}{4} \times \frac{1}{2} = \frac{1}{8}$. But I have 3 of these eighths to share so each person gets $3 \times \frac{1}{8} = \frac{3}{8}$ of a bar of candy.)

- *Did anyone think about part (1) a different way?* (I drew a picture. (Figure 2) I started with $\frac{3}{4}$. Each person gets half of the $\frac{3}{4}$, or $\frac{3}{8}$ of a candy bar. This is the same as $\frac{3}{4} \times \frac{1}{2} = \frac{3}{8}$.)

- *What do others think about this? Is $\frac{3}{4} \div 2 = \frac{3}{8}$ the same as $\frac{3}{4} \times \frac{1}{2} = \frac{3}{8}$? Is dividing by 2 the same as multiplying by $\frac{1}{2}$?* (yes)

- *What would be a reasonable estimate for how much each person will get in Question B, part (3)?* (Each person will get less than a half because you have three halves altogether and you have to share among four people.)

- *Why does part (3) have "Remember $1\frac{1}{2} = \frac{3}{2}$."* *in parentheses at the end of the problem?* (It is like when we multiplied and had to rewrite mixed numbers as fractions so that we could actually work with them. For example, when using the common denominator approach you need to know how many $\frac{1}{2}$'s there are in $1\frac{1}{2}$. You can show this by writing the mixed number as an improper fraction.)

- *Who can tell me their strategy for finding the answer to part (3)?* (You have $\frac{3}{2}$ to share among four people. So we need to find $\frac{3}{2} \div 4$. I drew a diagram and found that each person gets $\frac{3}{8}$.)

- *Is $\frac{3}{8}$ less than $\frac{1}{4}$?* ($\frac{1}{4}$ is equal to $\frac{2}{8}$, so $\frac{3}{8}$ is more.)

- *Did anyone use common denominators?* (I wrote $\frac{3}{2} \div 4 = \frac{3}{2} \div \frac{8}{2} = \frac{3}{8}$.)

Some students may write this one as $\frac{1\frac{1}{2}}{4}$. If they do, help them to see that this means $1\frac{1}{2} \div 4$, which is equivalent to $1\frac{1}{2} \times \frac{1}{4}$. Then we can write $1\frac{1}{2}$ as $\frac{3}{2}$ and have $\frac{3}{2} \times \frac{1}{4}$. Look for opportunities to express students' ideas as number sentences. Ask questions like the following:

- *Is $\frac{2}{5} \div 3$ equivalent to $\frac{2}{5} \times \frac{1}{3}$?*

- *Is $\frac{2}{5} \div 3$ equivalent to $\frac{2}{5} \div \frac{15}{5}$?*

Have students present their solutions and models for Question C. Use Question D to summarize an algorithm for dividing any fraction by any whole number. Some will see that multiplying by the reciprocal makes sense and works in both kinds of problems they have studied so far. Others will see this as multiplying by the denominator and dividing by the numerator of the divisor. Others may prefer to create common denominators and divide. Some will still need to draw pictures to help think through a problem.

Have students share the problems they wrote for Question E. Focus on why students think their problem represents the $\frac{8}{3} \div 4$. Discuss whether a problem is a sharing or grouping problem.

Figure 2

A whole candy bar

Three-fourths of a candy bar

Three-eighths of a candy bar for Person 1 and for Person 2

4.2 Fundraising Continues

Mathematical Goals

- Use models to represent a fraction divided by a whole number
- Develop and use strategies for dividing a fraction by a whole number
- Understand when division is an appropriate operation

Launch

- *Who can tell me how to change $\frac{3}{5}$ into a decimal? Why does that make sense?*

- *Fractions can be thought of as another way to show division. This means that $\frac{2}{3}$ can be thought of as $2 \div 3$. If you divide 2 by 3, you get $\frac{2}{3}$. Name a situation where this would be appropriate.*

- *In Investigation 3, we looked at products of two numbers that give exactly 1 as the answer. What did we call these number pairs?*

- *What is the reciprocal of $\frac{3}{5}$? Of 7? Of $4\frac{1}{3}$?*

Read Question A and remind students of things like drawing a diagram, labeling given quantities and answers, thinking about what you need to find and what you are given.

Have students work on Questions A and B individually and then in pairs to compare solutions and strategies and work on Questions C–E. If pressed for time, assign Questions C–E for homework and discuss the next day.

Explore

- *Do you see a pattern that would give you a short way of finding the answers?*

Help students see that the drawings and problems are similar to the ones done earlier but they start with a fractional part of something and share it among a whole number of people or entities equally. Ask if these are grouping or sharing problems.

Summarize

Have students illustrate how they did the divisions in Questions A and B.

Look for and, if necessary, create opportunities like the following solution a student provided for $\frac{1}{2} \div 4$ in Question A, part (1).

I drew a fraction strip to show $\frac{1}{2}$. Then I divided this amount into four parts. This lets me find $\frac{1}{4}$ of the amount because that is what each will get.

Materials
- Student notebooks

continued on next page

- *This diagram reminds me of the brownie pan problems in Investigation 3. What multiplication problem would this model represent?*

- *Why does it make sense that $\frac{1}{2} \div 4$ is the same as $\frac{1}{2} \times \frac{1}{4}$ which is $\frac{1}{8}$?*

Diagrams and reasoning like this help students move from division to multiplication of the reciprocal. Look at other approaches that students took to make sense of the problems. The problems in Question B use non-unit fractions.

- *How are the problems in Question B different from Question A?*

- *What would be a reasonable estimate for Question B part (3)?*

- *Why does Question B, part (3), have "Remember $1\frac{1}{2} = \frac{3}{2}$." in parentheses?*

Look for opportunities to express students' ideas as number sentences.

ACE Assignment Guide for Problem 4.2

Differentiated Instruction
Solutions for All Learners

Core 5–8, 30–34
Other *Applications* 9, 10; *Connections* 35; *Extensions* 41; unassigned choices from previous problems

Adapted For suggestions about adapting ACE exercises, see the CMP *Special Needs Handbook*.
Connecting to Prior Units 30, 35: *Bits and Pieces I*

Answers to Problem 4.2

See text of the Summary for supporting drawings.

A. 1. $\frac{1}{2} \div 4 = \frac{1}{8}$ lb

2. $\frac{1}{4} \div 3 = \frac{1}{12}$ lb

3. $\frac{1}{5} \div 2 = \frac{1}{10}$ lb

B. 1. $\frac{3}{4} \div 2 = \frac{3}{8}$ lb

2. $\frac{7}{8} \div 4 = \frac{7}{32}$ lb

3. $\frac{3}{2} \div 4 = \frac{3}{8}$ lb

C. 1. $\frac{1}{2} \div 4 = \frac{1}{8}$

2. $\frac{3}{2} \div 2 = \frac{3}{4}$

3. $\frac{2}{5} \div 3 = \frac{2}{15}$

4. $\frac{4}{5} \div 4 = \frac{4}{20}$ or $\frac{1}{5}$

D. Possible answers:

Multiply the first fraction by the reciprocal of the second fraction.

Multiply by the denominator of the second fraction and then divide by the numerator of the second fraction.

Rename the fractions to have common denominators and divide the numerators.

E. Answers will vary. One possibility is: Four brothers are sharing pizza. Their grandmother made three pizzas and ate $\frac{1}{3}$ of one before the boys got home. They shared the rest equally. How much did each brother get? Here, you have $\frac{8}{3}$ pizza to share among four brothers, but you have to realize that 3 whole pizzas minus the $\frac{1}{3}$ the grandmother ate leaves $2\frac{2}{3}$, or $\frac{8}{3}$, to share.

4.3 Summer Work

Goals

- Use models to represent a fraction divided by a fraction

- Develop and use strategies for dividing a fraction by a fraction

- Understand when division is an appropriate operation

  While fraction divided by fraction problems are conceptually and procedurally harder for students, the basis for understanding has been built through the first two problems, 4.1 and 4.2. You will want to continue to remind the students that they have ways of thinking that can be applied to these problems even though they are a bit different. The Launch-Explore-Summary will provide ways to have conversations about four different strategies. The strategies are: drawing a diagram, multiplying by the denominator and dividing by the numerator of the divisor, multiplying by the reciprocal, and using common denominators. All these strategies may not surface, and students do not need to be proficient with all of them.

Launch 4.3

Suggested Questions

- *We have already learned to divide fractions that have either the dividend or the divisor as a whole number. Now we are going to look at problems that involve two fractions.*

- *Suppose you have half of a large chocolate bar and your cookie recipe calls for $\frac{1}{8}$ of a bar. How many cookie recipes can you make with a half bar of chocolate? Think about this for a minute.*

- *What are we trying to find in this problem?* (How many $\frac{1}{8}$'s there are in $\frac{1}{2}$.)

- *Is this a sharing or a grouping problem? To decide, think about what the quantities in the problem are. What are you given and what are you trying to find?* (The quantities are the amount of chocolate bar that you have and the amount needed per recipe. You know the amount needed per batch. You are trying to find how many batches (groups) you can make that are of the size given. So, this is a grouping problem.)

- *Who has an idea about how to do this?* (Let's get common denominators. We can write the $\frac{1}{2}$ as $\frac{4}{8}$ and see immediately that there are four eighths in $\frac{1}{2}$. So the answer is 4 batches of cookies.)

- *How could we draw a diagram to show this?* (First, draw a fraction strip to show $\frac{1}{2}$ and then mark off parts equal to $\frac{1}{8}$. Oh, we will have to mark the bar into eighths! That is like finding a common denominator.)

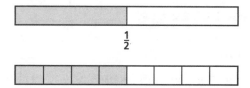

- *How does the diagram help us think about finding the quotient for $\frac{1}{2} \div \frac{1}{8}$?* (The bar is marked into eight equal pieces. Each is $\frac{1}{8}$. Now we can count to see that there are 4 eighths in the part of the bar that the cook has. So the cook can make four batches of cookies.)

- *Now I would like you to work on Question A, part (1) by yourselves. Then you can talk with your partners and share your strategies. For the rest of the questions, try each alone and then talk about what you did to your partner. Be prepared to explain your reasoning to the class.*

  If you are pressed for time, assign Questions D and E for homework. Be sure to have a conversation about them the next day.

INVESTIGATION 4

Explore 4.3

Circulate looking for students that need help and for those who have a good idea that should be shared in the summary. Remind them that diagrams can help make sense of the situation.

Suggested Questions Ask students questions like the following:

- *What are the quantities? What do you know and what are you trying to find?*

- *Is this a sharing or a grouping problem? Why?*

- *What kind of diagram will help?*

- *Is there a short cut for doing the problem that makes sense to you?*

When the students have completed most or all of the questions, bring them back together for a discussion of what they have found.

Summarize 4.3

Suggested Questions

- *Which question was harder, Question A or Question B? Why?* (Question B seemed harder because it took $\frac{2}{3}$ yd to make one bow. Unit fractions in Question A seem easier.)

- *Did your strategies have to change a lot for Question B?* (No. Actually the same ideas seemed to work.)

- *Are these sharing or grouping problems?* (They are grouping problems.)

- *Okay. Let's look at some of the problems. Who can tell me their strategy for solving Question A, part (1)?* (We need to find $\frac{1}{2} \div \frac{1}{6}$. We have $\frac{1}{2}$ yd of ribbon and we need $\frac{1}{6}$ yd per badge. This means we need to find how many sixths are in $\frac{1}{2}$. I drew a diagram and counted.)

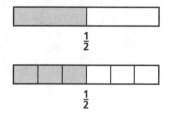

Ask if anyone drew their diagram a different way. For example:

- *We could mark off in the other direction. Either way shows that there are three $\frac{1}{6}$'s in $\frac{1}{2}$.*

- *Does anyone have another way to think about this one?* (I got a common denominator. So, I wrote $\frac{1}{2}$ as $\frac{3}{6}$. Then I had to find how many sixths are in $\frac{3}{6}$. This is the division problem, $\frac{3}{6} \div \frac{1}{6}$ or $3 \div 1$, which is 3.)

- *In Problem 4.2, we said that $\frac{2}{5} \div 3$ is equivalent to $\frac{2}{5} \times \frac{1}{3}$. Will this strategy work with the problem $\frac{1}{2} \div \frac{1}{6}$?* (Yes. If you rewrite $\frac{1}{6}$ as 6 and multiply $\frac{1}{2} \times 6$, you get 3 and the diagram shows that there are 3 one-sixths in $\frac{1}{2}$.)

- *Who can tell us about part (2) of Question A? What is different about this question?* (You have a non-unit fraction amount of ribbon.)

- *So do the same strategies work?* (Yes. You can still ask the question, "How many $\frac{1}{6}$'s are in $\frac{3}{4}$?" You can still draw a diagram, do common denominators, or multiply by the denominator and divide by the numerator of the divisor.)

- *Okay, play out your strategy for us.* (I used common denominators to write $\frac{3}{4}$ as $\frac{9}{12}$ and $\frac{1}{6}$ as $\frac{2}{12}$. Then I divided 9 by 2 to get $4\frac{1}{2}$ badges. Here is my picture.)

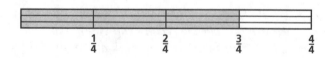

- *How does the diagram help us?* (I drew the three fourths of the whole and then divided the strip into thirds to make twelfths. Since $\frac{1}{6} = \frac{2}{12}$, I figured out how many $\frac{2}{12}$'s were in the $\frac{9}{12}$. I marked each group of $\frac{2}{12}$ differently so you can see there are $4\frac{1}{2}$.)

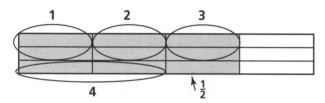

- *Some of you used the multiply by the denominator and divide by the numerator of the divisor strategy. Does that still work here?* [Yes. $\frac{3}{4} \div \frac{1}{6} = (\frac{3}{4} \times 6) \div 1 = \frac{18}{4} = 4\frac{2}{4} = 4\frac{1}{2}$ badges.]

If the students are having trouble with the remainder, go through the common denominator approach and draw a picture to help them see what is happening.

- *Let's have a volunteer talk about Question A, part (3). What is the answer and how did you find it?* (We need to find the number of $\frac{1}{6}$'s in $\frac{8}{3}$. It is easy if we find a common denominator. $\frac{8}{3}$ is equivalent to $\frac{16}{6}$, so we can make 16 badges.)

- *Now let's look at Question B. Here we need $\frac{2}{3}$ yard of ribbon for each bow. In part (1), we have $\frac{4}{5}$ yd of ribbon. What is the question we are trying to answer?* (How many $\frac{2}{3}$'s are in $\frac{4}{5}$?)

- *Are these grouping or sharing problems?* (They are all grouping problems because you are given a quantity to work with and how much each bow takes. You have to find the number of bows, which is like finding the number of groups.)

- *Tell us how you found the answer.* (I tried common denominators. I wrote both of the givens as 15ths. This gave me $\frac{10}{15}$ as the amount of ribbon each bow needed and $\frac{12}{15}$ as the amount of ribbon I have. So I have 12 parts and it takes 10 parts to make a bow. I can make 1 bow and have $\frac{2}{10}$ left over for another bow. This means I can make $1\frac{2}{10}$ bows.)

- *Anyone do it differently?* (I tried multiplying by the denominator and dividing by the numerator. This gave me $(\frac{4}{5} \times 3) \div 2$ which is $\frac{12}{5} \div 2$. This is the same as $\frac{12}{10}$, which is $1\frac{2}{10}$ of a bow.)

Ask similar questions for the remaining problems and ask for drawings where needed to help students make sense of the problems. As different strategies are used it is helpful to name them and make a list of them.

Use Question E to revisit or, if it has not emerged, discuss the common denominator approach. Depending on your students, if this approach was used in Questions A–C, it might be appropriate to discuss Elisha's claim then.

4.3 Summer Work

Mathematical Goals

- Use models to represent a fraction divided by a fraction
- Develop and use strategies for dividing a fraction by a fraction
- Understand when division is an appropriate operation

Launch

- *We have already learned to divide fractions that have a whole number for the dividend or divisor. Now we are going to look at problems that involve two fractions.*

- *Suppose you have half a large chocolate bar, and your recipe for cookies calls for $\frac{1}{8}$ of a bar. How many recipes can you make with a half bar of chocolate? What are we trying to find in this problem? Is this a sharing or grouping problem? How could we draw a diagram to show this?*

Have students work problems individually and then share their strategy and solution with a partner. If pressed for time, assign Questions D and E for homework, and discuss them the next day.

Explore

Look for strategies to use in the summary. Ask questions like the following:

- *What are the quantities? What do you know and what are you trying to find?*
- *Is this a sharing or grouping problem?*
- *What kind of diagram will help?*
- *Is there a shortcut for doing the problem that makes sense to you?*

Summarize

- *In which Questions were the problems harder, A or B? Why?*
- *Did your strategies have to change a lot for Question B?*
- *Are these grouping or sharing problems? Why?*
- *Who can share a strategy for solving Question A, part (1)?*

Be sure to ask students to talk about the meaning of quotient. Use diagrams to show what the remainder means in a solution like $2\frac{1}{2}$. If strategies from Problem 4.1 and 4.2 don't resurface, introduce them.

- *In Problem 4.2 we said that $\frac{2}{5} \div 3$ is equivalent to $\frac{2}{5} \times \frac{1}{3}$. Will this strategy work with the problem $\frac{1}{2} \div \frac{1}{6}$?*

Question E, Elisha's strategy, provides an opportunity to have a conversation about the common denominator approach, and why it works. Depending on your students, if this approach was used on Questions A–C, it might be appropriate to discuss Elisha's claim then.

Materials
- Student notebooks

ACE Assignment Guide for Problem 4.3

Core 11–14

Other *Connections* 36, 37; unassigned choices from previous problems

Adapted For suggestions about adapting ACE exercises, see the CMP *Special Needs Handbook*.

Answers to Problem 4.3

A. **1.** 3. $\frac{1}{2} \div \frac{1}{6} = 3$ ribbon badges; there will not be any extra ribbon.

2. $4\frac{1}{2}$. $\frac{3}{4} \div \frac{1}{6} = 4\frac{1}{2}$ ribbon badges; 4 whole ribbon badges and $\frac{1}{2}$ of a ribbon badge.

3. 16. $2\frac{2}{3} \div \frac{1}{6} = 16$ ribbon badges; there will not be any extra ribbon.

B. **1.** $1\frac{1}{5}$ bows

2. $2\frac{5}{8}$ bows

3. $3\frac{1}{2}$ bows

C. **1.** $\frac{9}{8}$ or $1\frac{1}{8}$

2. $\frac{14}{4}$ or $\frac{7}{2}$ or $3\frac{1}{2}$

3. $\frac{11}{3}$ or $3\frac{2}{3}$

D. Possible answers:

- Find a common denominator for each fraction. Then divide the numerator of the second fraction into the numerator of the first fraction.

- Multiply the first fraction by the denominator of the second fraction and divide the result by the numerator of the second fraction.

- Multiply the first fraction by the reciprocal of the second fraction.

E. **1.** Elisha's claim is correct. Possible explanation: The fractions in each problem are equivalent.

2. Elisha's claim is correct. Possible explanation: Elisha's new problem, $\frac{15}{20} \div \frac{8}{20}$ is asking how many groups of 8 twentieths can be made with 15 twentieths. This is the same as asking how many groups of 8 cookies can be made with 15 cookies. The number sentence for the cookie problem is $15 \div 8$.

3. Yes. $\frac{9}{15} \div \frac{5}{15} = \frac{9}{5}$, or $1\frac{4}{5}$

4.4 Writing a Division Algorithm

Goals

- Develop an efficient algorithm to solve any fraction division problem

- Explore the inverse operations of multiplication and division

This problem is structured like Problem 2.4 and 3.5 where students worked with pre-sorted addition, subtraction, and multiplication problems to develop an algorithm. Students are given a table with four groups of division problems. Each group has something in common that needs to be considered when dividing fractions.

    Group 1: fractions divided by whole numbers
    Group 2: whole numbers divided by fractions
    Group 3: fractions divided by fractions
    Group 4: mixed number and fraction division
            problems

Question B provides additional practice in using the algorithm students develop for division. Question C asks students to write a complete multiplication-division fact family given a complete fraction division problem. Question D asks students to use the inverse relationships and their multiplication and division algorithms to solve missing-value problems.

Understanding the inverse relationship between addition and subtraction is easier and more intuitive to students than multiplication and division relationships. In Investigation 3, ACE Exercise 36 was included to get students to think about multiplication-division fact families. If you did not assign or have a conversation about this problem it could be helpful to use it as a warm-up or to assign it as homework and discuss it before working on Questions C and D of Problem 4.4.

The goal of ACE 36 is to get students to think about how inverse relationships can be used as a tool even when the numbers seemed slightly unfamiliar. For example, most students can write the complete fact family for $3 \times 6 = 18$ and are comfortable in doing so because $3 \times 6 = 18$ is a basic fact they have had lots of experience with. When given a problem with greater numbers or more complex numbers, such as fractions, students can become unsure. Help students realize that the

numbers are irrelevant if they understand how multiplication and division are related.

Let's look at the problem $1\frac{1}{2} \times 7 = 10\frac{1}{2}$ and compare it to $3 \times 6 = 18$. Most students are comfortable switching the position of the factors to create the corresponding multiplication problems.

$$a \times b = c \qquad b \times a = c$$
$$3 \times 6 = 18 \qquad 6 \times 3 = 18$$
$$1\tfrac{1}{2} \times 7 = 10\tfrac{1}{2} \qquad 7 \times 1\tfrac{1}{2} = 10\tfrac{1}{2}$$

When writing the corresponding division problems for each fact family, it is helpful to focus on the factor-product relationship. When dividing the product of the original multiplication problem by one factor you will get the other factor. Using the problem $3 \times 6 = 18$ can help students make sense of this relationship in a problem like $1\frac{1}{2} \times 7 = 10\frac{1}{2}$.

$$3 \times 6 = 18: \qquad 18 \div 3 = 6 \text{ and } 18 \div 6 = 3$$
$$a \times b = c: \qquad c \div a = b \text{ and } c \div b = a$$
$$1\tfrac{1}{2} \times 7 = 10\tfrac{1}{2}: \; 10\tfrac{1}{2} \div 1\tfrac{1}{2} = 7 \text{ and } 10\tfrac{1}{2} \div 7 = 1\tfrac{1}{2}$$

When working on the missing-value problems in Question D of Problem 4.4, focus on using the inverse relationship of multiplication and division. Returning to familiar whole number problems can be helpful here, too.

$$3 \times 6 = 18 \quad 18 \div 3 = 6 \quad 18 \div 6 = 3$$
$$a \times b = c \quad c \div a = b \quad c \div b = a$$
$$N \times \tfrac{7}{8} = \tfrac{3}{4} \quad \tfrac{3}{4} \div N = \tfrac{7}{8} \quad \tfrac{3}{4} \div \tfrac{7}{8} = N$$

Here the problem, $\frac{3}{4} \div \frac{7}{8} = N$, provides a way to find the missing value. Students may struggle with these problems and that is okay since this is the first of several experiences they will have with inverse relationships. Keep in mind that students may need to return many times to whole number problems that they are comfortable with for this relationship to become natural and sensible.

Launch 4.4

Remind students of the work they did in Problems 2.4 and 3.5. Explain that they are going to do a similar problem to develop a general algorithm for dividing fractions. Use Transparency 4.4 to display the table with the sorted division problems and read through the questions of Problem 4.4 making sure students know what to do.

Depending on your students, you might want to work on Questions A–C, stop and summarize before doing Question D. To start, have students work Question A, part (1) individually. Then finish the problem in pairs or small groups.

Explore 4.4

Suggested Questions As students work, pay attention to what they think each group has in common. Ask questions that help students articulate what the groups have in common and why their algorithms make sense. Also note how students are approaching Question C.

- *What do you think all these problems have in common?*

- *Show me a problem that does not fit in this category.*

- *Why do you think your new problem fits in Group 2?*

- *What method did you use to solve the problem?*

- *Why do you think that method works?*

As groups develop their general algorithms, note whether they are general enough to account for cases that include whole numbers, mixed numbers, and fractions. Have students write their algorithms on blank transparencies or chart paper so they can use them during the summary. Ask them to include example problems that show that their algorithm will work for each of the four groups.

Summarize 4.4

Begin by looking at the chart in Question A. Discuss what they think each of the groups have in common and discuss their examples of other problems that belong in each group. Then move to discussing their general algorithms.

Suggested Questions Questions such as the following can be used:

- *Can someone describe what the problems in Group 1 have in common? In Group 2? In Group 3?*

- *Would someone like to share your division algorithm?*

- *This group has described a general algorithm that uses common denominators. Did anyone else use this approach? Do you agree with their algorithm? Would you change anything in their algorithm?*

- *Did another group develop another algorithm that will work for all division cases?*

As students share the general algorithms they put on transparencies or large sheets of chart paper, you may want to develop a master list of the algorithms that students developed.

Have students share the fact family they made for Question C. Focus on how students reorganized the multiplication problem to find the division problems.

- *What are the factors in the problem $\frac{2}{3} \times \frac{4}{5} = \frac{8}{15}$?* $(\frac{2}{3}$ and $\frac{4}{5})$

- *How can the problem $2 \times 4 = 8$ help you rearrange this problem into a division problem?* (8 is the product. If you divide the product by one factor, you will get the other factor. So, $8 \div 4 = 2$ or $8 \div 2 = 4$. In $\frac{2}{3} \times \frac{4}{5} = \frac{8}{15}$, $\frac{8}{15}$ is the product. If you divide it by one of the factors, you will get the other factor.)

With Question D, also focus on how multiplication and division are related. Use whole numbers to help students make sense of the problems. Some students may use a common denominator approach to division when trying to find missing values. For example with $\frac{3}{4} \div N = \frac{7}{8}$, students may rewrite the problem as $\frac{6}{8} \div \frac{7}{8} = N$.

- *What did you think about when you rewrote $\frac{3}{4} \div N = \frac{7}{8}$ as $\frac{6}{8} \div \frac{7}{8} = N$?* (First, I rewrote $\frac{3}{4}$ as $\frac{6}{8}$ so the problem would have common denominators. Then, I knew that $6 \div 3$ equals 2 and $6 \div 2$ gives the other factor of 3, so I knew I could divide $\frac{6}{8}$ by $\frac{7}{8}$ and get the missing amount for N.)

- *How can you figure out what N is?* (Figure out $6 \div 7$.)

- *What is $6 \div 7$?* ($\frac{6}{7}$)

- *Does $6 \div \frac{6}{7} = 7$?* (yes)

- *Why?* (Because there are 42 sevenths in 6 wholes, and it takes 6 sevenths to make $\frac{6}{7}$. Since $42 \div 6 = 7$, this gives seven $\frac{6}{7}$'s in 6.)

The same questioning can be used if students work with $\frac{3}{4} \div N = \frac{7}{8}$ as it is. Other students may try to use reciprocals. Help students focus on using the inverse relationships of multiplication and division to identify which values represent the factors and the product in the multiplication problem that is part of the fact family.

4.4 Writing a Division Algorithm

Mathematical Goals

- Develop an efficient algorithm to solve any fraction division problem
- Explore the inverse operations of multiplication and division

Launch

Remind students of the work they did in Problems 2.4 and 3.5. Explain that in this problem they will develop an algorithm for dividing fractions. Use Transparency 4.4 to display the sorted division problems. Read the questions of the problem making sure students know what to do. You may want students to work on Questions A–C, and then stop and summarize before doing Question D. To start, have students complete Question A, part (1) individually and then work in small groups to develop an algorithm.

Materials
- Transparency 4.4

Vocabulary
- algorithm (revisited)

Explore

Ask questions that help students articulate what the groups have in common and why their algorithms made sense. Also note how students are approaching Question C.

- *What do you think all these problems have in common?*
- *Show me a problem that does not fit in this category.*
- *Why do you think your new problem fits in Group 2?*
- *What method did you use to solve the problem?*
- *Why do you think that method works?*

Have students put their algorithms on chart paper or transparencies.

Materials
- Large chart paper or blank transparencies
- Markers

Summarize

- *Can someone describe what the problems in Group 1 have in common? In Group 2? In Group 3?*
- *Would someone like to share their division algorithm?*
- *This group has described an algorithm that uses common denominators? Did anyone else use this approach? Do you agree with their algorithm? Would you change anything in their algorithm?*
- *Did another group develop an algorithm that would work for all division cases?*

Have students share the fact family they made for Question C. Focus on how students reorganize the multiplication problem to find division problems.

- *What are the factors in $\frac{2}{3} \times \frac{4}{5} = \frac{8}{15}$?*
- *How can the problem $2 \times 4 = 8$ help you rearrange this problem into a division problem?*

Materials
- Student notebooks

continued on next page

With Question D, help students focus on using the inverse relationships of multiplication and division to identify which values represent the factors and the product in the multiplication problem that is part of the fact family. Here a student used the common denominator approach.

- *What did you think about when you rewrote $\frac{3}{4} \div N = \frac{7}{8}$ as $\frac{6}{8} \div \frac{7}{8} = N$?*
- *How can you figure out what N is?*
- *What is $6 \div 7$?*
- *Does $6 \div \frac{6}{7} = 7$? Why?*

ACE Assignment Guide for Problem 4.4

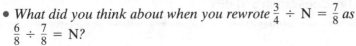

Core 15–23
Other *Connections* 38, *Extensions* 39, 40; unassigned choices from previous problems

Adapted For suggestions about adapting ACE exercises, see the CMP *Special Needs Handbook*.
Connecting to Prior Units 38: *Bits and Pieces I*

Answers to Problem 4.4

A. 1.

Group 1	Group 2	Group 3	Group 4
$\frac{1}{27}$	72	10	$3\frac{1}{3}$
$\frac{1}{72}$	$\frac{15}{2}$ or $7\frac{1}{2}$	1	$\frac{3}{22}$
$\frac{3}{30}$ or $\frac{1}{10}$	$\frac{15}{2}$ or $7\frac{1}{2}$	$3\frac{3}{5}$	5

2. Group 1: fractions divided by whole numbers

Group 2: whole numbers divided by fractions

Group 3: fractions divided by fractions

Group 4: mixed number and fraction division problems

3. Answers will vary.

4. Answers will vary. Most likely students will use one of the three algorithms discussed in the teacher notes: reciprocal approach, multiply by the denominator and divide by the numerator, or common denominators. Check to be sure the algorithms are general enough to account for cases with mixed numbers, whole numbers and fractions.

B. 1. $9 \div \frac{4}{5} = 11\frac{1}{4}$

2. $1\frac{7}{8} \div 3 = \frac{5}{8}$

3. $1\frac{2}{3} \div \frac{1}{5} = 8\frac{1}{3}$

4. $2\frac{5}{6} \div 1\frac{1}{3} = 2\frac{1}{8}$

C. 1. $\frac{2}{3} \times \frac{4}{5} = \frac{8}{15}, \frac{4}{5} \times \frac{2}{3} = \frac{8}{15}, \frac{8}{15} \div \frac{4}{5} = \frac{2}{3}$, and $\frac{8}{15} \div \frac{2}{3} = \frac{4}{5}$

2. Check students' work.

D. 1. $N = \frac{10}{12}$ or $\frac{5}{6}$

2. $N = \frac{6}{7}$

3. $N = \frac{3}{4}$

The student edition pages for this
investigation begin on the next page.

Notes _____

_____

_____

_____

Dividing With Fractions

In earlier investigations of this unit, you learned to use addition, subtraction, and multiplication of fractions in a variety of situations. There are times when you also need to divide fractions. To develop ideas about when and how to divide fractions, let's review the meaning of division in problems involving only whole numbers.

Getting Ready for Problem 4.1

Students at Lakeside Middle School raise funds to take a field trip each spring. In each of the following fundraising examples, explain how you recognize what operation(s) to use. Then write a number sentence to show the required calculations.

- The 24 members of the school swim team get dollar-per-mile pledges for a swim marathon they enter. The team goal is to swim 120 miles. How many miles should each swimmer swim?

- There are 360 students going on the field trip. Each school bus carries 30 students. How many buses are needed?
- The school band plans to sell 600 boxes of cookies. There are 20 members in the band. How many boxes should each member sell to reach the goal if each sells the same number of boxes?

Compare your number sentences and reasoning about these problems with classmates. Decide which are correct and why.

Notes _____

_____

_____

_____

4.1 Preparing Food

There are times when the amounts given in a division situation are not whole numbers but fractions. First, you need to understand what division of fractions means. Then you can learn how to calculate quotients when the divisor or the dividend, or both, is a fraction.

When you do the division $12 \div 5$, what does the answer mean?

The answer should tell you how many fives are in 12 wholes. Because there is not a whole number of fives in 12, you might write:

$$12 \div 5 = 2\frac{2}{5}$$

Now the question is, what does the *fractional part* of the answer mean?

The answer means you can make 2 fives and $\frac{2}{5}$ *of another five.*

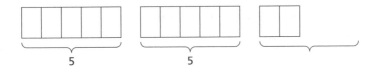

Suppose you ask, "How many $\frac{3}{4}$'s are in 14?" You can write this as a division problem, $14 \div \frac{3}{4}$.

Can you make a whole number of $\frac{3}{4}$'s out of 14 wholes?

If not, what does the fractional part of the answer mean?

As you work through the problems in this investigation, keep these two questions in mind.

What does the answer to a division problem mean?

What does the fractional part of the answer to a division problem mean?

Notes

Use written explanations or diagrams to show your reasoning for each part. Write a number sentence showing your calculation(s).

A. Naylah plans to make small cheese pizzas to sell at a school fundraiser. She has nine bars of cheese. How many pizzas can she make if each pizza needs the given amount of cheese?

1. $\frac{1}{3}$ bar   **2.** $\frac{1}{4}$ bar   **3.** $\frac{1}{5}$ bar

4. $\frac{1}{6}$ bar   **5.** $\frac{1}{7}$ bar   **6.** $\frac{1}{8}$ bar

B. Frank also has nine bars of cheese. How many pizzas can he make if each pizza needs the given amount of cheese?

1. $\frac{1}{3}$ bar   **2.** $\frac{2}{3}$ bar   **3.** $\frac{3}{3}$ bar   **4.** $\frac{4}{3}$ bar

5. The answer to part (2) is a mixed number. What does the fractional part of the answer mean?

C. Use what you learned from Questions A and B to complete the following calculations.

1. $12 \div \frac{1}{3}$ **2.** $12 \div \frac{2}{3}$ **3.** $12 \div \frac{5}{3}$

4. $12 \div \frac{1}{6}$ **5.** $12 \div \frac{5}{6}$ **6.** $12 \div \frac{7}{6}$

7. The answer to part (3) is a mixed number. What does the fractional part of the answer mean in the context of cheese pizzas?

D. 1. Explain why $8 \div \frac{1}{3} = 24$ and $8 \div \frac{2}{3} = 12$.

2. Why is the answer to $8 \div \frac{2}{3}$ exactly half the answer to $8 \div \frac{1}{3}$?

E. Write an algorithm that seems to make sense for dividing any whole number by any fraction.

F. Write a story problem that can be solved using $12 \div \frac{2}{3}$. Explain why the calculation matches the story.

ACE Homework starts on page 55.

4.2 Fundraising Continues

While figuring prizes for the games at their fundraiser, students and teachers face more fraction problems!

Notes _____

_____

_____

_____

Problem 4.2 Dividing a Fraction by a Whole Number

Use written explanations or diagrams to show your reasoning for each part. Write a number sentence showing your calculation(s).

A. Ms. Li brings peanuts to be shared equally by members of groups winning each game. How much of a pound of peanuts will each student get in the given situations?

1. Four students share $\frac{1}{2}$ pound of peanuts.

2. Three students share $\frac{1}{4}$ pound of peanuts.

3. Two students share $\frac{1}{5}$ pound of peanuts.

B. A popcorn store donates its different-sized boxes of popcorn for use as prizes at a team competition. How much popcorn does each team member get in the given situations?

1. A two-person team shares a $\frac{3}{4}$-pound box of popcorn equally.

2. A four-person team shares a $\frac{7}{8}$-pound box of popcorn equally.

3. A four-person team shares a $1\frac{1}{2}$-pound box of popcorn equally.
   (Remember $1\frac{1}{2} = \frac{3}{2}$.)

C. Find each quotient and explain which model you used.

1. $\frac{1}{2} \div 4$ **2.** $\frac{3}{2} \div 2$

3. $\frac{2}{5} \div 3$ **4.** $\frac{4}{5} \div 4$

D. What algorithm makes sense for dividing any fraction by any whole number?

E. Write a story problem that can be solved by $\frac{8}{3} \div 4$. Explain why the calculation matches the story.

ACE **Homework starts on page 55.**

Investigation 4 Dividing With Fractions   **51**

STUDENT PAGE

STUDENT PAGE

Notes _____

_____

_____

_____

(51) 114

4.3 Summer Work

In Problems 4.1 and 4.2, you developed ways of thinking about and solving division problems involving a whole number and a fraction. In the next problem, the questions involve division of a fraction by another fraction.

Problem 4.3 Dividing a Fraction by a Fraction

Rasheed and Ananda have summer jobs at a ribbon company. Answer the questions below. Use written explanations or diagrams in each to show your reasoning. Write a number sentence to show your calculation(s).

A. Rasheed takes a customer order for ribbon badges. It takes $\frac{1}{6}$ yard to make a ribbon for a badge. How many ribbon badges can he make from the given amounts of ribbon? Describe what each fractional part of an answer means.

1. $\frac{1}{2}$ yard

2. $\frac{3}{4}$ yard

3. $2\frac{2}{3}$ yards (Remember $2\frac{2}{3} = \frac{8}{3}$.)

Notes _____

_____

_____

_____

B. Ananda is working on an order for bows. She uses $\frac{2}{3}$ yard of ribbon to make one bow. How many bows can Ananda make from each of the following amounts of ribbon?

1. $\frac{4}{5}$ yard   **2.** $1\frac{3}{4}$ yards   **3.** $2\frac{1}{3}$ yards

C. Solve each of the following examples as if they were ribbon problems.

1. $\frac{3}{4} \div \frac{2}{3}$ **2.** $1\frac{3}{4} \div \frac{1}{2}$ **3.** $2\frac{3}{4} \div \frac{3}{4}$

D. What algorithm makes sense for dividing any fraction by any fraction?

E. To solve $\frac{3}{4} \div \frac{2}{5}$, Elisha writes, "$\frac{3}{4} \div \frac{2}{5}$ is the same as $\frac{15}{20} \div \frac{8}{20}$. So the answer to $\frac{3}{4} \div \frac{2}{5}$ is the same as $15 \div 8$."

1. Is Elisha's first claim, that $\frac{3}{4} \div \frac{2}{5}$ is the same as $\frac{15}{20} \div \frac{8}{20}$, correct?

2. Is his second claim, that the answer to $\frac{3}{4} \div \frac{2}{5}$ is the same as $15 \div 8$, correct?

3. Use Elisha's method to solve $\frac{3}{5} \div \frac{1}{3}$. Does the method give a correct solution?

ACE Homework starts on page 55.

4.4 Writing a Division Algorithm

You are ready now to develop an algorithm for dividing fractions. To get started, you will break division problems into categories and write steps for each kind of problem. Then you can see whether there is one "big" algorithm that will solve them all.

Notes _____

_____

_____

_____

A. 1. Find the quotients in each group below.

Group 1	Group 2	Group 3	Group 4
$\frac{1}{3} \div 9$	$12 \div \frac{1}{6}$	$\frac{5}{6} \div \frac{1}{12}$	$5 \div 1\frac{1}{2}$
$\frac{1}{6} \div 12$	$5 \div \frac{2}{3}$	$\frac{3}{4} \div \frac{3}{4}$	$\frac{1}{2} \div 3\frac{2}{3}$
$\frac{3}{5} \div 6$	$3 \div \frac{2}{5}$	$\frac{9}{5} \div \frac{1}{2}$	$3\frac{1}{3} \div \frac{2}{3}$

2. Describe what the problems in each group have in common.

3. Make up one new problem that fits in each group.

4. Write an algorithm that works for dividing *any* two fractions, including mixed numbers. Test your algorithm on the problems in the table. If necessary, change your algorithm until you think it will work all the time.

B. Use your algorithm to divide.

1. $9 \div \frac{4}{5}$　　　**2.** $1\frac{7}{8} \div 3$　　　**3.** $1\frac{2}{3} \div \frac{1}{5}$　　　**4.** $2\frac{5}{6} \div 1\frac{1}{3}$

C. Here is a multiplication-division fact family for whole numbers:

$5 \times 8 = 40$　　　$8 \times 5 = 40$　　　$40 \div 5 = 8$　　　$40 \div 8 = 5$

1. Complete this multiplication-division fact family for fractions.

$$\frac{2}{3} \times \frac{4}{5} = \frac{8}{15}$$

2. Check the division answers by using your algorithm.

D. For each number sentence, find a value for N that makes the sentence true. If needed, use fact families.

1. $\frac{2}{3} \div \frac{4}{5} = N$　　　**2.** $\frac{3}{4} \div N = \frac{7}{8}$　　　**3.** $N \div \frac{1}{4} = 3$

ACE **Homework starts on page 55.**

STUDENT PAGE

Notes _____

_____

_____

_____

Applications

1. The Easy Baking Company makes muffins. Some are small and some are huge. There are 20 cups of flour in the packages of flour they buy. How many muffins can be made from a package of flour if each takes the following amounts of flour?

   a. $\frac{1}{4}$ cup
   b. $\frac{2}{4}$ cup
   c. $\frac{3}{4}$ cup

   d. $\frac{1}{10}$ cup
   e. $\frac{2}{10}$ cup
   f. $\frac{7}{10}$ cup

   g. $\frac{1}{7}$ cup
   h. $\frac{2}{7}$ cup
   i. $\frac{6}{7}$ cup

   j. Explain how the answers for $20 \div \frac{1}{7}$, $20 \div \frac{2}{7}$, and $20 \div \frac{6}{7}$ are related. Show why this makes sense.

2. Find each quotient.

   a. $6 \div \frac{3}{5}$
   b. $5 \div \frac{2}{9}$
   c. $3 \div \frac{1}{4}$
   d. $4 \div \frac{5}{8}$

3. For parts (a)–(c), do the following steps:

   • Draw pictures or write number sentences to show why your answer is correct.

   • If there is a remainder, tell what the remainder means for the situation.

   a. Bill is making 22 small pizzas for a party. He has 16 cups of flour. Each pizza crust takes $\frac{3}{4}$ cup of flour. Does he have enough flour?

   b. There are 12 baby rabbits at the pet store. The manager lets Gabriella feed vegetables to the rabbits as treats. She has $5\frac{1}{4}$ ounces of parsley today. She wants to give each rabbit the same amount. How much parsley does each rabbit get?

   c. It takes $18\frac{3}{8}$ inches of wood to make a frame for a small snapshot. Ms. Jones has 3 yards of wood. How many frames can she make?

Investigation 4 Dividing With Fractions   **55**

Notes _____

_____

_____

_____

4. Find each quotient. Describe any patterns that you see.

    a. $5 \div \frac{1}{4}$ **b.** $5 \div \frac{1}{8}$ **c.** $5 \div \frac{1}{16}$

5. Maria uses $5\frac{1}{3}$ gallons of gas to drive to work and back four times.

    a. How many gallons of gas does Maria use in one round trip to work?

    b. Maria's car gets 28 miles to the gallon. How many miles is her round trip to work?

6. Anoki is in charge of giving prizes to teams at a mathematics competition. With each prize, he also wants to give each member of the team an equal amount of mints. How much will each team member get if Anoki has the given amounts of mints?

    a. $\frac{1}{2}$ pound of mints for 8 students

    b. $\frac{1}{4}$ pound of mints for 4 students

    c. $\frac{3}{4}$ pound of mints for 3 students

    d. $\frac{4}{5}$ pound of mints for 10 students

    e. $1\frac{1}{2}$ pounds of mints for 2 students

7. **Multiple Choice** Nana's recipe for applesauce makes $8\frac{1}{2}$ cups. She serves the applesauce equally among her three grandchildren. How many cups of applesauce will each one get?

    A. $\frac{3}{2}$ cups   **B.** $25\frac{1}{2}$ cups   **C.** $\frac{9}{6}$ cups   **D.** Not here

8. Divide. Draw a picture to prove that each quotient makes sense.

    a. $\frac{4}{5} \div 3$ **b.** $1\frac{2}{3} \div 5$ **c.** $\frac{5}{3} \div 5$

9. **Multiple Choice** Which of the following diagrams represents $4 \div \frac{1}{3}$?

    F.   **G.**   **H.**   **J.**

STUDENT PAGE

Notes _____

_____

_____

_____

10. Multiple Choice Which of the following diagrams represents $\frac{1}{3} \div 4$?

A.

B.

C.

D.

11. A latte (LAH tay) is the most popular coffee drink at Antonio's Coffee Shop.

Antonio makes only one size latte, and he uses $\frac{1}{3}$ cup of milk to make each drink. For parts (a)–(c), find:

- How many lattes he can make with the amount of milk given.
- What the remainder means, if there is one.

a. $\frac{7}{9}$ cup   **b.** $\frac{5}{6}$ cup   **c.** $3\frac{2}{3}$ cups

12. Write a story problem that can be solved using $1\frac{3}{4} \div \frac{1}{2}$. Explain why the calculation matches your story.

For: Help with Exercise 12
Web Code: ame-4412

13. Find each quotient.

a. $\frac{5}{6} \div \frac{1}{3}$ **b.** $\frac{2}{3} \div \frac{1}{9}$ **c.** $1\frac{1}{2} \div \frac{3}{8}$

Investigation 4 Dividing With Fractions   **57**

Notes _____

_____

_____

_____

14. Is each quotient greater than or less than 1? Explain.

a. $\dfrac{7}{9} \div \dfrac{1}{9}$ b. $\dfrac{2}{3} \div \dfrac{1}{9}$ c. $\dfrac{1}{18} \div \dfrac{1}{9}$ d. $1 \div \dfrac{1}{9}$

Go Online
PHSchool.com

For: Multiple-Choice Skills Practice
Web Code: ama-4454

For Exercises 15–20, find the quotient.

15. $10 \div \dfrac{2}{3}$ **16.** $5 \div \dfrac{3}{4}$ **17.** $\dfrac{6}{7} \div 4$

18. $\dfrac{3}{10} \div 2$ **19.** $\dfrac{2}{5} \div \dfrac{1}{3}$ **20.** $2\dfrac{1}{2} \div 1\dfrac{1}{3}$

21. For Exercises 15 and 17 above, write a story problem to fit the computation.

Write a complete multiplication-division fact family.

22. $\dfrac{2}{3} \times \dfrac{5}{7} = \dfrac{10}{21}$ **23.** $\dfrac{3}{4} \div 1\dfrac{1}{2} = \dfrac{1}{2}$

Connections

24. Mr. Delgado jogs $2\dfrac{2}{5}$ km on a trail and then sits down to wait for his friend Mr. Prem. Mr. Prem has jogged $1\dfrac{1}{2}$ km down the trail. How much farther will Mr. Prem have to jog to reach Mr. Delgado?

25. Toshi has to work at the car wash for 3 hours. So far, he has worked $1\dfrac{3}{4}$ hours. How many more hours before he can leave work?

58   Bits and Pieces II

Notes _____

_____

_____

_____

For Exercises 26–29, find each sum or difference. Then, give another fraction that is equivalent to the answer.

26. $\frac{9}{10} + \frac{1}{5}$ **27.** $\frac{5}{6} + \frac{7}{8}$ **28.** $\frac{2}{3} + 1\frac{1}{3}$ **29.** $12\frac{5}{6} - 8\frac{1}{4}$

30. Every fraction can be written in many equivalent forms. For example, $\frac{12}{15}$ is equivalent to $\frac{24}{30}$. For each fraction, find two equivalent fractions. One fraction should have a numerator greater than the one given. The other fraction should have a numerator less than the one given.

     a. $\frac{4}{6}$ **b.** $\frac{10}{12}$ **c.** $\frac{12}{9}$ **d.** $\frac{8}{6}$

Find each product.

31. $\frac{2}{7} \times \frac{1}{3}$ **32.** $\frac{3}{4} \times \frac{7}{8}$ **33.** $1\frac{1}{2} \times \frac{1}{3}$ **34.** $4\frac{2}{3} \times 2\frac{3}{4}$

35. The marks on each number line are spaced so that the distance between two consecutive marks is the same. Copy each number line and label the marks.

     a.

```
    ┌──┼────┼────┼────┼────┼──►
      1.8                    2
```

     b.

```
    ┌──┼────┼────┼────┼────┼──►
      1                    1.1
```

     c.

```
    ┌──┼────┼────┼────┼────┼──►
      2.93                2.95
```

     d.

```
    ┌──┼────┼────┼────┼────┼──►
      1.99                2.01
```

     e. Explain how you determined what the labels should be.

36. By what number should you multiply to get 1 as the product?

     a. $2 \times \blacksquare = 1$ **b.** $\frac{1}{2} \times \blacksquare = 1$ **c.** $3 \times \blacksquare = 1$

     d. $\frac{1}{3} \times \blacksquare = 1$ **e.** $\blacksquare \times \frac{2}{3} = 1$ **f.** $\frac{3}{4} \times \blacksquare = 1$

     g. $\blacksquare \times \frac{5}{2} = 1$ **h.** $1\frac{1}{4} \times \blacksquare = 1$ **i.** $\frac{7}{12} \times \blacksquare = 1$

Notes _____

_____

_____

_____

37. Find the missing numbers in each pair. What is the relationship between each pair?

a. $3 \div \blacksquare = 9$

$3 \times \blacksquare = 9$

b. $3 \div \blacksquare = 12$

$3 \times \blacksquare = 12$

c. $2\frac{1}{2} \div \blacksquare = 5$

$2\frac{1}{2} \times \blacksquare = 5$

38. Use the cartoon to answer the questions below.

a. How many slices of the pizza will have olives?

b. How many slices of the pizza will be plain?

c. What fraction of the pizza will have onions and green peppers?

Extensions

39. DonTae says that when you want to find out how many quarters are in some whole number of dollars, you should divide the number of dollars by $\frac{1}{4}$. Vanna says that you need to multiply the number of dollars by 4. With whom do you agree? Why?

40. Find a value for N that makes the sentence true. Don't forget fact families.

a. $N \times \frac{1}{5} = \frac{2}{15}$

b. $N \div \frac{1}{5} = \frac{2}{3}$

c. $\frac{1}{2} \times N = \frac{1}{3}$

d. $\frac{1}{5} \div N = \frac{1}{3}$

e. $1\frac{3}{4} \div N = \frac{1}{4}$

f. $2\frac{2}{3} \div N = 8$

Notes

41. Use the table below to solve parts (a)–(e).

Measurement	Equivalent Measurement
1 cup	16 tablespoons
1 quart	4 cups
1 quart	2 pints
1 gallon	4 quarts
1 tablespoon	3 teaspoons

a. Brian is missing his measuring cup. He needs to measure out $\frac{1}{2}$ cup of vegetable oil. How many tablespoons should he use?

b. How many teaspoons does Brian need to use to measure out $\frac{1}{2}$ cup of vegetable oil?

c. What fraction of a quart is $\frac{1}{2}$ cup?

d. What fraction of a gallon is $\frac{1}{2}$ cup?

e. Suppose you need to measure out exactly one gallon of water. The only measuring cups you have are $\frac{1}{2}$ cup, 1 cup, and 1 pint. Which measuring cup would you use? How would you make sure you had exactly one gallon?

Notes _____

_____

_____

_____

Mathematical Reflections 4

In this investigation, you developed strategies for dividing with fractions. You developed algorithms that can be used to divide any two fractions or mixed numbers. These questions will help you to summarize what you have learned.

Think about your answers to these questions. Discuss your ideas with other students and your teacher. Then write a summary of your findings in your notebook.

1. Explain your algorithm for dividing two fractions. Demonstrate your algorithm with an example for each situation.
   - a whole number divided by a fraction
   - a fraction divided by a whole number
   - a fraction divided by a fraction
   - a mixed number divided by a fraction

2. Explain why the following example can be solved using division.

   A local coffee house donates $2\frac{2}{3}$ pounds of gourmet coffee beans to be sold at a local fundraiser. The people running the fundraiser decide to package and sell the coffee beans in $\frac{1}{2}$-pound packages. How many $\frac{1}{2}$-pound packages can they make?

3. How is the quotient of $20 \div \frac{1}{5}$ related to the quotient of $20 \div \frac{3}{5}$? Explain.

Notes _____

_____

_____

_____

Investigation

ACE
Assignment Choices

Differentiated Instruction
Solutions for All Learners

Problem 4.1
Core 1, 2, 24–29
Other *Applications* 3, 4

Problem 4.2
Core 5–8, 30–34
Other *Applications* 9–10, *Connections* 35, *Extensions* 41; unassigned choices from previous problems

Problem 4.3
Core 11–14
Other *Connections* 36, 37; unassigned choices from previous problems

Problem 4.4
Core 15–23
Other *Connections* 38; *Extensions* 39, 40; unassigned choices from previous problems

Adapted For suggestions about adapting Exercise 1 and other ACE exercises, see the CMP *Special Needs Handbook*.
Connecting to Prior Units 30, 35, 38: *Bits and Pieces I*

Applications

1. a. $20 \div \frac{1}{4} = 80$ muffins

    b. $20 \div \frac{2}{4} = 40$ muffins

    c. $20 \div \frac{3}{4} = 26\frac{2}{3}$ muffins

    d. $20 \div \frac{1}{10} = 200$ muffins

    e. $20 \div \frac{2}{10} = 100$ muffins

    f. $20 \div \frac{7}{10} = 28\frac{4}{7}$ muffins

    g. $20 \div \frac{1}{7} = 140$ muffins

    h. $20 \div \frac{2}{7} = 70$ muffins

i. $20 \div \frac{6}{7} = 23\frac{1}{3}$ muffins

j. Since the muffins made when using $\frac{2}{7}$ of a cup of flour are twice as large as the muffins made when using $\frac{1}{7}$ of a cup of flour, you will need twice as much flour. But you don't have twice as much flour; you only have one bag. You will have to make half a recipe, which yields half as many muffins. If you make muffins using $\frac{6}{7}$ of a cup of flour, it takes six times as much flour as the muffins made with $\frac{1}{7}$ of a cup. If it takes six times as much flour, you will only be able to make $\frac{1}{6}$ the number of muffins as the recipe with $\frac{1}{7}$ of a cup or $140 \div 6 = 23\frac{1}{3}$ muffins.

2. a. $6 \div \frac{3}{5} = 10$ **b.** $5 \div \frac{2}{9} = 22\frac{1}{2}$

    c. $3 \div \frac{1}{4} = 12$ **d.** $4 \div \frac{5}{8} = 6\frac{2}{5}$

3. a. No. $16 \div \frac{3}{4} = \frac{64}{4} \div \frac{3}{4} = 21\frac{1}{3}$ pizzas. He has enough flour to make 21 complete pizzas and $\frac{1}{3}$ of another pizza.

    b. $5\frac{1}{4} \div 12 = \frac{21}{4} \div 12 = \frac{21}{4} \div \frac{48}{4} = \frac{21}{48}$ or $\frac{7}{16}$ ounce of parsley

    c. 3 yards is 108 inches.
$108 \div 18\frac{3}{8} = 108 \div \frac{147}{8} = \frac{864}{8} \div \frac{147}{8}$, which is $\frac{864}{147}$ or $\frac{288}{49} = 5\frac{43}{49}$.

    The remainder tells us that Ms. Jones can make 5 complete frames and $\frac{43}{49}$ of another frame, or Ms. Jones can make 5 complete frames and will have $16\frac{1}{8}$ in. of molding left over.

4. a. $5 \div \frac{1}{4} = 20$ **b.** $5 \div \frac{1}{8} = 40$

    c. $5 \div \frac{1}{16} = 80$

Possible explanation: In each case, the divisor is half of the previous divisor. This means that twice as many can be found in 5. For example, $5 \div \frac{1}{4} = 20$. In the next problem you are dividing by eighths and eighths are half the size of fourths so twice as many can go into 5.

5. a. $5\frac{1}{3} \div 4 = 1\frac{1}{3}$ gallons per trip

    b. $28 \times 1\frac{1}{3} = 37\frac{1}{3}$ mi

6. a. $\frac{1}{2} \div 8 = \frac{1}{16}$ pound per student

    b. $\frac{1}{4} \div 4 = \frac{1}{16}$ pound per student

    c. $\frac{3}{4} \div 3 = \frac{1}{4}$ pound per student

    d. $\frac{4}{5} \div 10 = \frac{4}{50}$ or $\frac{2}{25}$ pound per student

    e. $1\frac{1}{2} \div 2 = \frac{3}{4}$ pound per student

7. D

8. a. $\frac{4}{5} \div 3 = \frac{4}{15}$; Possible diagram: This diagram is made by renaming $\frac{4}{5}$ as $\frac{12}{15}$. Since there are 12 fifteenths, you can divide by 3 or group the fifteenths into 3 groups. Each of the three groups will have 4 fifteenths in it.

$\frac{1}{15}$ $\frac{1}{15}$	$\frac{1}{15}$ $\frac{1}{15}$	$\frac{1}{15}$ $\frac{1}{15}$
$\frac{1}{15}$ $\frac{1}{15}$	$\frac{1}{15}$ $\frac{1}{15}$	$\frac{1}{15}$ $\frac{1}{15}$

    b. $1\frac{2}{3} \div 5 = \frac{1}{3}$; Possible diagram: This diagram shows $1\frac{2}{3}$ as 5 thirds. Since you are dividing by 5, you can make 5 groups. Each group will have $\frac{1}{3}$ in it.

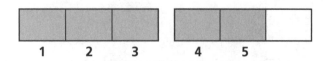

1   2   3   4   5

    c. $\frac{5}{3} \div 5 = \frac{1}{3}$; This problem is equivalent to 8b, so you can use the same diagram.

9. F

10. C

11. a. $\frac{7}{9} \div \frac{1}{3} = 2\frac{1}{3}$ lattes, which means 2 full lattes and $\frac{1}{3}$ of another

    b. $\frac{5}{6} \div \frac{2}{6} = 2\frac{1}{2}$ lattes, which means 2 full lattes and $\frac{1}{2}$ of another

    c. $3\frac{2}{3} \div \frac{1}{3} = 11$ lattes

12. Possible answer: Josh is cooking for his nephews and wants to make as many recipes of chili as he can from the $1\frac{3}{4}$ cup of dried beans that he has on hand. Each recipe takes $\frac{1}{2}$ cup of dried beans. How many recipes can he make? Here you have to find $1\frac{3}{4} \div \frac{1}{2}$, or how many halves are in $1\frac{3}{4}$. There are 3 full batches and half of another, or $3\frac{1}{2}$ batches.

13. a. $\frac{5}{6} \div \frac{1}{3} = 2\frac{1}{2}$

    b. $\frac{2}{3} \div \frac{1}{9} = 6$

    c. $1\frac{1}{2} \div \frac{3}{8} = 4$

14. a. greater than 1; $\frac{7}{9}$ is made with many $\frac{1}{9}$ parts

    b. greater than 1; if you rename $\frac{2}{3}$ as $\frac{6}{9}$, there are many $\frac{1}{9}$'s in $\frac{6}{9}$.

    c. less than 1; 18ths are smaller than 9ths so $\frac{1}{9}$ will not fit or go into $\frac{1}{18}$ a whole time.

    d. greater than 1; since 9ths are smaller than 1, more than 1 ninth will fit into 1 whole.

15. $10 \div \frac{2}{3} = 15$ **16.** $5 \div \frac{3}{4} = 6\frac{2}{3}$

17. $\frac{6}{7} \div 4 = \frac{3}{14}$ **18.** $\frac{3}{10} \div 2 = \frac{3}{20}$

19. $\frac{2}{5} \div \frac{1}{3} = 1\frac{1}{5}$ **20.** $2\frac{1}{2} \div 1\frac{1}{3} = 1\frac{7}{8}$

21. Exercise 15: I have a 10-ft roll of paper to make signs. If each sign takes $\frac{2}{3}$ ft of paper, how many signs can I make?

Exercise 17: I bought $\frac{6}{7}$ pound of jellybeans. If I wanted to share them with three other people, how much of a pound will each of us get?

22. $\frac{2}{3} \times \frac{5}{7} = \frac{10}{21}, \frac{5}{7} \times \frac{2}{3} = \frac{10}{21}, \frac{10}{21} \div \frac{2}{3} = \frac{5}{7}$, and $\frac{10}{21} \div \frac{5}{7} = \frac{2}{3}$

23. $\frac{3}{4} \div 1\frac{1}{2} = \frac{1}{2}, \frac{3}{4} \div \frac{1}{2} = 1\frac{1}{2}, 1\frac{1}{2} \times \frac{1}{2} = \frac{3}{4}$; and $\frac{1}{2} \times 1\frac{1}{2} = \frac{3}{4}$

Connections

24. $2\frac{2}{5} - 1\frac{1}{2} = \frac{9}{10}$ km

25. $3 - 1\frac{3}{4} = 1\frac{1}{4}$ hours

26. $\frac{11}{10}$ or $1\frac{1}{10}$ (equivalent fractions will vary)

27. $\frac{41}{24}$ or $1\frac{17}{24}$ (equivalent fractions will vary)

28. 2 or $\frac{6}{3}$ (equivalent fractions will vary)

29. $4\frac{7}{12}$ (equivalent fractions will vary)

30. a. Possible answers: $\frac{2}{3}$ and $\frac{8}{12}$

    b. Possible answers: $\frac{5}{6}$ and $\frac{20}{24}$

    c. Possible answers: $\frac{4}{3}$ and $\frac{24}{18}$

    d. Possible answers: $\frac{4}{3}$ and $\frac{16}{12}$

31. $\frac{2}{21}$ **32.** $\frac{21}{32}$

33. $\frac{3}{6}$ or $\frac{1}{2}$ **34.** $\frac{154}{12}$ or $12\frac{10}{12}$ or $12\frac{5}{6}$

35. a.

    1.8   1.85   1.9   1.95   2

    b.

    1   1.025   1.05   1.075   1.1

    c.

    2.93   2.935   2.94   2.945   2.95

    d.

    1.99   1.995   2   2.005   2.01

    e. To find the difference between two consecutive marks, take the difference between the two end points and divide by 4 because there are four equal divisions between the two endpoints. Then add that amount to the left endpoint to find the value for the first mark. Add that same value to that answer, and then add that amount once more to the next answer.

36. The numbers in each pair are reciprocals of each other.

    a. Possible answer: $\frac{1}{2}$

    b. Possible answer: 2

    c. Possible answer: $\frac{1}{3}$

    d. Possible answer: 3

    e. Possible answer: $\frac{3}{2}$

    f. Possible answer: $\frac{4}{3}$

    g. Possible answer: $\frac{2}{5}$

    h. Possible answer: $\frac{4}{5}$

    i. Possible answer: $\frac{12}{7}$ or $1\frac{5}{7}$

37. The numbers in each pair are reciprocals of each other.

    a. $\frac{1}{3}$ and 3

    b. $\frac{1}{4}$ and 4

    c. $\frac{1}{2}$ and 2

38. a. 3; $37\frac{1}{2}$% of the pizza is $\frac{3}{8}$ of the 8 slices or 3 slices.

    b. 1; $\frac{3}{24} = \frac{1}{8}$. The pizza has 8 slices and $\frac{1}{8}$ of 8 slices is 1 slice.

    c. $\frac{1}{2}$; 4 of the 8 pieces have other two toppings. 4 out of 8, or $\frac{1}{2}$ of the pizza, have onions and green peppers.

Extensions

39. Both DonTae and Vanna are correct. Dividing a number by $\frac{1}{4}$ is equivalent to multiplying by the reciprocal of $\frac{1}{4}$, or 4.

40. a. $N = \frac{2}{3}$ **b.** $N = \frac{2}{15}$

   c. $N = \frac{2}{3}$ **d.** $N = \frac{3}{5}$

   e. $N = 7$ **f.** $N = \frac{1}{3}$

41. a. 8 tablespoons   **b.** 24 teaspoons

   c. $\frac{1}{8}$ quart   **d.** $\frac{1}{32}$

   e. Answers may vary. A $\frac{1}{2}$-cup measure would need to be used 32 times, a one-cup measure 16 times, and a 1-pint measure 8 times.

Possible Answers to Mathematical Reflections

1. Students may have different algorithms at this stage. Two algorithms that may develop are included.

Find a common denominator and then divide the numerators. Examples:

$5 \div \frac{1}{3} = \frac{15}{3} \div \frac{1}{3} = 15$

$\frac{2}{3} \div 4 = \frac{2}{3} \div \frac{12}{3} = 2 \div 12 = \frac{2}{12}$ or $\frac{1}{6}$

$\frac{2}{3} \div \frac{1}{2} = \frac{4}{6} \div \frac{3}{6} = 4 \div 3 = \frac{4}{3}$ or $1\frac{1}{3}$

$1\frac{1}{2} \div \frac{2}{7} = \frac{3}{2} \div \frac{2}{7} = \frac{21}{14} \div \frac{4}{14} = 21 \div 4 = 5\frac{1}{4}$

Recognize that dividing by a number is the same as multiplying by its reciprocal.

$5 \div \frac{1}{3} = 5 \times 3 = 15$

$\frac{2}{3} \div 4 = \frac{2}{3} \times \frac{1}{4} = \frac{2}{12}$ or $\frac{1}{6}$

$\frac{2}{3} \div \frac{1}{2} = \frac{2}{3} \times 2 = \frac{4}{3}$ or $1\frac{1}{3}$

$1\frac{1}{2} \div \frac{2}{7} = \frac{3}{2} \div \frac{2}{7} = \frac{3}{2} \times \frac{7}{2} = \frac{21}{4} = 5\frac{1}{4}$

2. The situation is a grouping problem. It is asking how many groups of $\frac{1}{2}$ can be made from $2\frac{2}{3}$. This is like asking how many times $\frac{1}{2}$ can go into $2\frac{2}{3}$.

3. Since it takes three $\frac{1}{5}$'s to make $\frac{3}{5}$, the answer to $20 \div \frac{1}{5}$ is three times as large as the answer to $20 \div \frac{3}{5}$. So, take the answer to $20 \div \frac{1}{5}$ (which is the same as $20 \times 5 = 100$) and divide this by three to get the answer to $20 \div \frac{3}{5}$. The quotient is $\frac{100}{3}$ or $33\frac{1}{3}$.

Answers to Looking Back and Looking Ahead

1. a. Since the total weight of the nuts is 2 pounds, Jayne's bill was $10.

   b. peanuts: $\frac{1}{4}$

      almonds: $\frac{1}{6}$

      pecans: $\frac{1}{8}$

      hazelnuts: $\frac{1}{12}$

      cashews: $\frac{3}{8}$

   c. Diego buys $1\frac{1}{4}$ pound of nuts and it costs $6.25.

   d. Kalli has enough nuts to make $13\frac{1}{2}$ bowls or 13 whole bowls.

2. a. Shaquille orders $2\frac{3}{4}$ lb of dried fruit. (dried peaches: $\frac{1}{2}$ lb, dried cherries: $\frac{4}{10}$, or $\frac{2}{5}$ lb, dried pineapple: $\frac{6}{12}$ or $\frac{1}{2}$ lb, dried apple rings: $\frac{27}{20}$, or $1\frac{7}{20}$ lb)

   b. $13.75

3. To find the cost of Jayne's mix, you have to add the number of pounds of each type of nut together to get 2 lb. Since nuts are $5.00 per pound, I doubled or multiplied by 2 to get the total cost of $10.

4. Since the fractions in the problem were part of 1 lb, the fraction of 2 lb would be half of the original because the number of pounds or the size of the whole has doubled.

For example, $\frac{1}{3}$ of one pound is only $\frac{1}{6}$ of 2 lb. I noticed that I just need to double the denominator of each of the original fraction to get the fraction of 2 lb.

5. In $4 \div \frac{1}{3} = 12$, you are finding how many one-thirds are in 4. There are 12 one-thirds in 4. In $4 \div \frac{2}{3} = 6$ you are finding how many times two-thirds, something that is twice as big as one-third, goes into 4. Since what you are dividing by is twice as big, the answer will be twice as small, or 6 instead of 12.

6. a. $\frac{5}{6} + \frac{1}{4} = \frac{10}{12} + \frac{3}{12} = \frac{13}{12}$; You can solve this problem by renaming the fractions so they have like denominators and then adding the numerators. Put the sum of the numerators over the like denominator.

b. $\frac{3}{4} - \frac{2}{3} = \frac{9}{12} - \frac{8}{12} = \frac{1}{12}$; You can solve this problem by renaming the fractions so they have like denominators and then subtracting the numerators. Put the difference of the numerators over the like denominator.

c. $\frac{2}{5} \times \frac{3}{8} = \frac{6}{40} = \frac{3}{20}$; You can solve this problem by multiplying the numerators to find the numerator of the answer and multiplying the denominators to find the denominator of the answer.

d. $\frac{3}{8} \div \frac{3}{4} = \frac{3}{8} \times \frac{4}{3} = \frac{12}{24} = \frac{1}{2}$; One way to divide fractions is to multiply the first fraction by the reciprocal of the second fraction. In this problem the reciprocal of $\frac{3}{4}$ is $\frac{4}{3}$. Once the problem is changed into a multiplication problem, follow the algorithm for multiplying fractions.

Looking Back and Looking Ahead

Unit Review

The problems in this unit helped you develop strategies for estimating and computing with fractions. You learned how to identify situations that call for computation with fractions. You developed algorithms for adding, subtracting, multiplying, and dividing fractions. You learned how to solve problems with fractions. Use what you have learned to solve the following examples.

Go Online
PHSchool.com
For: Vocabulary Review Puzzle
Web Code: amj-4051

Use Your Understanding: Fraction Operations

1. The Scoop Shop sells many types of nuts. Jayne asks for this mix:

   $\frac{1}{2}$ pound peanuts $\frac{1}{6}$ pound hazelnuts

   $\frac{1}{3}$ pound almonds $\frac{3}{4}$ pound cashews

   $\frac{1}{4}$ pound pecans

   a. Nuts cost $5.00 per pound. What is Jayne's bill?

   b. What fraction of the mix does each kind of nut represent?

   c. Diego does not like cashews, so he asks for Jayne's mix without the cashews. What is his bill?

   d. Kalli is making small bowls of nuts for a party. Each bowl uses $\frac{1}{4}$ cup of nuts. Kalli has $3\frac{3}{8}$ cups of nuts. How many bowls can she make?

STUDENT PAGE

Notes _____

_____

_____

_____

2. Shaquille likes dried fruit. He wants a mix of peaches, cherries, pineapple chunks, and apple rings. The following chart shows how much The Scoop Shop has of each fruit and how much of each fruit Shaquille orders.

The Scoop Shop's Stock	Shaquille's Order
$1\frac{1}{2}$ pounds dried peaches	$\frac{1}{3}$ of the stock
$\frac{4}{5}$ pound dried cherries	$\frac{1}{2}$ of the stock
$\frac{3}{4}$ pound dried pineapple chunks	$\frac{2}{3}$ of the stock
$2\frac{1}{4}$ pounds dried apple rings	$\frac{3}{5}$ of the stock

a. How many pounds of dried fruit does Shaquille order?

b. Dried fruit cost $5.00 per pound. What is Shaquille's bill?

Explain Your Reasoning

When you use mathematical calculations to solve a problem or make a decision, it is important to be able to support each step in your reasoning.

3. What operations did you use to find the cost of the nuts in Jayne's mix?

4. How did you find the fraction of the mix for each kind of nut?

5. $4 \div \frac{1}{3} = 12$ and $4 \div \frac{2}{3} = 6$. Why is the second answer half of the first?

6. Use the following problems to show the steps involved in algorithms for adding, subtracting, multiplying, and dividing fractions. Be prepared to explain your reasoning.

a. $\frac{5}{6} + \frac{1}{4}$ b. $\frac{3}{4} - \frac{2}{3}$ c. $\frac{2}{5} \times \frac{3}{8}$ d. $\frac{3}{8} \div \frac{3}{4}$

Notes _____

_____

_____

_____

Look Ahead

The ideas and techniques you have used in this unit will be applied and expanded in future units of *Connected Mathematics*, in other mathematics work in school, and in your future work. Fractions are used in measuring and calculating quantities of all kinds—from length, area, and volume to time, money, test scores, and weights.

Looking Back and Looking Ahead   **65**

Notes

English / Spanish Glossary

A

algorithm A set of rules for performing a procedure. Mathematicians invent algorithms that are useful in many kinds of situations. Some examples of algorithms are the rules for long division or the rules for adding two fractions. The following algorithm was written by a middle-grade student:

To add two fractions, first change them to equivalent fractions with the same denominator. Then add the numerators and put the sum over the common denominator.

algoritmo Un conjunto de reglas para realizar un procedimiento. Los matemáticos inventan algoritmos que son útiles en muchos tipos de situaciones. Algunos ejemplos de algoritmos son las reglas para una división larga o las reglas para sumar dos fracciones. El siguiente es un algoritmo escrito por un estudiante de un grado intermedio.

Para sumar dos fracciones, primero transfórmalas en fracciones equivalentes con el mismo denominador. Luego suma los numeradores y coloca la suma sobre el denominador común.

B

benchmark A "nice" number that can be used to estimate the size of other numbers. For work with fractions, 0, $\frac{1}{2}$, and 1 are good benchmarks. We often estimate fractions or decimals with benchmarks because it is easier to do arithmetic with them, and estimates often give enough accuracy for the situation. For example, many fractions and decimals—such as $\frac{37}{50}$, $\frac{5}{8}$, 0.43, and 0.55—can be thought of as being close to $\frac{1}{2}$. You might say $\frac{5}{8}$ is between $\frac{1}{2}$ and 1 but closer to $\frac{1}{2}$, so you can estimate $\frac{5}{8}$ to be about $\frac{1}{2}$. We also use benchmarks to help compare fractions. For example, we could say that $\frac{5}{8}$ is greater than 0.43 because $\frac{5}{8}$ is greater than $\frac{1}{2}$ and 0.43 is less than $\frac{1}{2}$.

punto de referencia Un número "bueno" que se puede usar para estimar el tamaño de otros números. Para trabajar con fracciones, 0, $\frac{1}{2}$ y 1 son buenos puntos de referencia. Por lo general estimamos fracciones o decimales con puntos de referencia porque nos resulta más fácil hacer cálculos aritméticos con ellos, y las estimaciones suelen ser bastante exactas para la situación. Por ejemplo, muchas fracciones y decimales, como por ejemplo $\frac{37}{50}$, $\frac{5}{8}$, 0.43 y 0.55, se pueden considerar como cercanos a $\frac{1}{2}$. Se podría decir que $\frac{5}{8}$ está entre $\frac{1}{2}$ y 1, pero más cerca de $\frac{1}{2}$, por lo que se puede estimar que $\frac{5}{8}$ es alrededor de $\frac{1}{2}$. También usamos puntos de referencia para ayudarnos a comparar fracciones. Por ejemplo, podríamos decir que $\frac{5}{8}$ es mayor que 0.43, porque $\frac{5}{8}$ es mayor que $\frac{1}{2}$ y 0.43 es menor que $\frac{1}{2}$.

Notes

denominator The number written below the line in a fraction. In the fraction $\frac{3}{4}$, 4 is the denominator. In the part-whole interpretation of fractions, the denominator shows the number of equal-sized parts into which the whole has been split.

denominador El número escrito debajo de la línea en una fracción. En la fracción $\frac{3}{4}$, 4 es el denominador. En la interpretación de partes y enteros de fracciones, el denominador muestra el número de partes iguales en que fue dividido el entero.

E

equivalent fractions Fractions that are equal in value, but may have different numerators and denominators. For example, $\frac{2}{3}$ and $\frac{14}{21}$ are equivalent fractions. The shaded part of this rectangle represents both $\frac{2}{3}$ and $\frac{14}{21}$.

fracciones equivalentes Fracciones de igual valor, que pueden tener diferentes numeradores y denominadores. Por ejemplo, $\frac{2}{3}$ y $\frac{14}{21}$ son fracciones equivalentes. La parte sombreada de este rectángulo representa tanto $\frac{2}{3}$ como $\frac{14}{21}$.

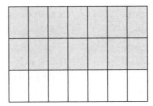

F

fact family A set of related addition-subtraction sentences or multiplication-division sentences. For example, the set of numbers 3, 5, and 15 are part of this multiplication-division fact family:

$$3 \times 5 = 15 \qquad 5 \times 3 = 15$$
$$15 \div 5 = 3 \qquad 15 \div 3 = 5$$

If you have one fact from a family, you can use the addition-subtraction or multiplication-division relationship to write the three related facts that are also part of the family. For example, with $2 + 3 = 5$, you can use the relationship between addition and subtraction to write the related number sentences $3 + 2 = 5, 5 - 3 = 2$, and $5 - 2 = 3$.

familia de datos Conjunto de oraciones de suma y resta o de multiplicación y división relacionadas. Por ejemplo, el grupo de números 3, 5 y 15 son parte de esta familia de datos de multiplicación y división:

$$3 \times 5 = 15 \qquad 5 \times 3 = 15$$
$$15 \div 5 = 3 \qquad 15 \div 3 = 5$$

Si tienes un dato de una familia, puedes usar la relación entre la suma y la resta, y entre la multiplicación y división para escribir los tres datos relacionados que también son parte de la familia. Por ejemplo, con $2 + 3 = 5$, puedes usar la relación entre la suma y la resta para escribir las oraciones numéricas relacionadas $3 + 2 = 5, 5 - 3 = 2$ y $5 - 2 = 3$.

English/Spanish Glossary **67**

Notes _____

_____

_____

numerator The number written above the line in a fraction. In the fraction $\frac{5}{8}$, 5 is the numerator. When you interpret the fraction $\frac{5}{8}$ as a part of a whole, the numerator 5 tells that the fraction refers to 5 of the 8 equal parts.

numerador El número escrito sobre la línea en una fracción. En la fracción $\frac{5}{8}$, 5 es el numerador. Cuando interpretas una fracción como $\frac{5}{8}$ como parte de un entero, el numerador 5 te dice que la fracción se refiere a 5 de 8 partes iguales.

reciprocal A factor by which you multiply a given number so that their product is 1. For example, $\frac{3}{5}$ is the reciprocal of $\frac{5}{3}$, and $\frac{5}{3}$ is the reciprocal of $\frac{3}{5}$ because $\frac{3}{5} \times \frac{5}{3} = 1$. Note that the reciprocal of $1\frac{2}{3}$ is $\frac{3}{5}$ because $1\frac{2}{3} \times \frac{3}{5} = 1$.

número recíproco Un factor por el cual multiplicas un número dado de manera que su producto sea 1. Por ejemplo, $\frac{3}{5}$ es el número recíproco de $\frac{5}{3}$, y $\frac{5}{3}$ es el número recíproco de $\frac{3}{5}$, porque $\frac{3}{5} \times \frac{5}{3} = 1$. Fíjate que el recíproco de $1\frac{2}{3}$ es $\frac{3}{5}$, porque $1\frac{2}{3} \times \frac{3}{5} = 1$.

unit fraction A fraction with a numerator of 1. For example, in the unit fraction $\frac{1}{13}$, the part-whole interpretation of fractions tells us that the whole has been split into 13 equal-sized parts, and that the fraction represents the quantity of 1 of those parts.

fracción de unidad Una fracción con numerador 1. Por ejemplo, en la fracción de unidad $\frac{1}{13}$, la interpretación de fracciones de una parte entera nos indica que el entero ha sido dividido en 13 partes iguales y que la fracción representa la cantidad 1 de esas partes.

Notes _____

_____

_____

_____

STUDENT PAGE

Academic Vocabulary

The following terms are important to your understanding of the mathematics in this unit. Knowing and using these words will help you in thinking, reasoning, representing, communicating your ideas, and making connections across ideas. When these words make sense to you, the investigations and problems will make more sense as well.

E

explain To give facts and details that make an idea easier to understand. Explaining can involve a written summary supported by a diagram, chart, table, or a combination of these.

related terms: analyze, clarify, describe, justify, tell

Sample: **Explain why the answer to $12 \div \frac{3}{4}$ is one third the answer to $12 \div \frac{1}{4}$.**

Because $\frac{3}{4} = 3 \times \frac{1}{4}$, it takes three $\frac{1}{4}$s to make every $\frac{3}{4}$. There are forty-eight $\frac{1}{4}$s in 12, but there are only sixteen $\frac{3}{4}$s in 12.

explicar Dar hechos y detalles que hacen que una idea sea más fácil de comprender. Explicar puede implicar un resumen escrito apoyado por un diagrama, una gráfica, una tabla o una combinación de éstos.

términos relacionados: analizar, aclarar, describir, justificar, decir

Ejemplo: **Explica por qué la respuesta a $12 \div \frac{3}{4}$ es un tercio de la respuesta a $12 \div \frac{1}{4}$.**

Porque $\frac{3}{4} = 3 \times \frac{1}{4}$, se requieren tres $\frac{1}{4}$ para formar cada $\frac{3}{4}$. Hay cuarenta y ocho $\frac{1}{4}$ en 12, pero sólo hay dieciséis $\frac{3}{4}$ en 12.

M

model To represent a situation using pictures, diagrams, or number sentences.

related terms: represent, demonstrate

Sample: **Yolanda has one half of an apple pie. She eats one third of the half pie. Model this situation using a number sentence or a picture.**

I can write one third as $\frac{1}{3}$ and half as $\frac{1}{2}$, so one third of one half can be written as $\frac{1}{3} \times \frac{1}{2}$. Because $\frac{1}{3} \times \frac{1}{2} = \frac{1}{6}$, she eats $\frac{1}{6}$ of the entire pie.

I can also divide a whole fraction strip into halves, then divide each half into thirds.

$\frac{1}{2}$		$\frac{1}{2}$	

$\frac{1}{6}$	$\frac{1}{6}$	$\frac{1}{6}$	$\frac{1}{6}$	$\frac{1}{6}$	$\frac{1}{6}$

Yolanda eats $\frac{1}{6}$ of the entire pie.

hacer modelos Representar una situación usando imágenes, diagramas u oraciones numéricas.

términos relacionados: representar, demostrar

Ejemplo: **Yolanda tiene una mitad de una tarta de manzana. Se come un tercio de la mitad de la tarta. Haz un modelo de esta situación usando una oración numérica o una imagen.**

Puedo escribir un tercio como $\frac{1}{3}$ y la mitad como $\frac{1}{2}$, así que un tercio de una mitad puede escribirse como $\frac{1}{3} \times \frac{1}{2}$. Debido a que $\frac{1}{3} \times \frac{1}{2} = \frac{1}{6}$, ella se come $\frac{1}{6}$ de la tarta entera. También puedo dividir una tira de fracciones entera en mitades, luego divido cada mitad en tercios.

$\frac{1}{2}$		$\frac{1}{2}$	

$\frac{1}{6}$	$\frac{1}{6}$	$\frac{1}{6}$	$\frac{1}{6}$	$\frac{1}{6}$	$\frac{1}{6}$

Yolanda se come $\frac{1}{6}$ de la tarta entera.

Academic Vocabulary **69**

Notes _____

_____

_____

_____

reason To think through using facts and information.
related terms: think, examine, logic

Sample: To find the number of $\frac{1}{2}$-cup servings in 6 cups, Jenni says it is necessary to multiply 6 by $\frac{1}{2}$. Zach says that 6 must be divided by $\frac{1}{2}$ to find the number of servings. With whom do you agree? Explain how you reasoned.

> I agree with Zach because you want to know how many halves there are in 6. This question is answered by division: $6 \div \frac{1}{2} = 12$. Multiplying 6 by $\frac{1}{2}$ separates it into 2 equal parts of 3 each. That is not what is asked for in the question.

razonar Considerar usando hechos e información.
términos relacionados: pensar, examinar, lógica

Ejemplo: Para hallar el número de porciones de $\frac{1}{2}$ taza en 6 tazas, Jenni dice que es necesario multiplicar 6 por $\frac{1}{2}$. Zach dice que 6 debe dividirse entre $\frac{1}{2}$ para hallar el número de porciones. ¿Con quién estás de acuerdo? Explica cómo hiciste tu razonamiento.

> Estoy de acuerdo con Zach porque se desea saber cuántas mitades hay en 6. Esta pregunta se responde por división: $6 \div \frac{1}{2} = 12$. Multiplicar 6 por $\frac{1}{2}$ lo separa en 2 partes iguales de 3 cada una. Esto no es lo que se pide en la pregunta.

---

recall To remember a fact quickly.
related terms: remember, recognize

Sample: Mateo wants to add 0.3 to $\frac{1}{2}$. What can you recall about $\frac{1}{2}$ or 0.3 that will help him find the sum? Explain.

> I recall that $\frac{1}{2}$ is equivalent to the decimal 0.5. When both numbers are in decimal form, they can be added easily. Mateo can add $0.5 + 0.3$ to get 0.8.
> I also recall that 0.3 is the same as $\frac{3}{10}$ and $\frac{1}{2}$ is equivalent to $\frac{5}{10}$. Mateo can add $\frac{3}{10} + \frac{5}{10}$ to get $\frac{8}{10}$ which is the same as 0.8.
>

recordar Acordarse rápido de un hecho.
términos relacionados: acordarse, reconocer

Ejemplo: Mateo desea sumar 0.3 a $\frac{1}{2}$. ¿Qué puedes recordar sobre $\frac{1}{2}$ o 0.3 que le ayudará a hallar la suma? Explica tu respuesta.

> Recuerdo que $\frac{1}{2}$ es equivalente al decimal 0.5. Cuando ambos números están en forma decimal, pueden sumarse con facilidad. Mateo puede sumar $0.5 + 0.3$ para obtener 0.8.
> También recuerdo que 0.3 is igual a $\frac{3}{10}$ y $\frac{1}{2}$ es equivalente a $\frac{5}{10}$. Mateo puede sumar $\frac{3}{10} + \frac{5}{10}$ para obtener $\frac{8}{10}$, que es igual a 0.8.
>

70 Bits and Pieces II

Notes

Notes _____

Notes

Acknowledgments

Team Credits

The people who made up the **Connected Mathematics2** team—representing editorial, editorial services, design services, and production services—are listed below. Bold type denotes core team members.

Leora Adler, Judith Buice, Kerry Cashman, Patrick Culleton, Sheila DeFazio, Richard Heater, **Barbara Hollingdale, Jayne Holman,** Karen Holtzman, **Etta Jacobs,** Christine Lee, Carolyn Lock, Catherine Maglio, **Dotti Marshall,** Rich McMahon, Eve Melnechuk, Kristin Mingrone, Terri Mitchell, **Marsha Novak,** Irene Rubin, Donna Russo, Robin Samper, Siri Schwartzman, **Nancy Smith,** Emily Soltanoff, **Mark Tricca,** Paula Vergith, Roberta Warshaw, Helen Young

Additional Credits

Diana Bonfilio, Mairead Reddin, Michael Torocsik, nSight, Inc.

Technical Illustration

WestWords, Inc.

Cover Design

tom white.images

Photos

2 t, Courtesy of JCL Equipment Co. Inc.; **2 b,** GK Hart/Vikki Hart/Getty Images, Inc.; **3,** Ed Young/Corbis; **7,** Richard Haynes; **8,** Syracuse Newspapers/The Image Works; **17,** PhotoDisc/PictureQuest; **19,** Paul Hardy/Corbis; **22,** Richard Haynes; **29,** E.R. Degginger/Bruce Coleman, Inc.; **32,** Richard Haynes; **35,** Courtesy of JCL Equipment Co. Inc.; **37,** Russ Lappa; **41,** L. Clarke/Corbis; **43,** Tony Freeman/PhotoEdit; **48,** Tony Freeman/PhotoEdit; **51 l,** Dorling Kindersley; **51 r,** Royalty-Free/Corbis; **52,** Ed Scott/AGE Fotostock; **55,** GK Hart/Vikki Hart/Getty Images, Inc.; **58,** Eric Bean/Getty Images, Inc.; **60,** ©2001, Hilary B. Price. Distributed by King Features Syndicate, Inc.; **61,** Silver Burdett Ginn; **63,** Russ Lappa

Note: Every effort has been made to locate the copyright owner of the material reprinted in this book. Omissions brought to our attention will be corrected in subsequent editions.

Acknowledgments **73**

Notes _____

_____

_____

_____

Labsheet 1.1A

Getting Close Cards

$\frac{1}{10}$	$\frac{1}{8}$	$\frac{1}{5}$	$\frac{1}{4}$	$\frac{1}{3}$
$\frac{1}{2}$	$\frac{3}{10}$	$\frac{7}{10}$	$\frac{9}{10}$	$\frac{2}{5}$
$\frac{3}{5}$	$\frac{4}{9}$	1	$\frac{3}{4}$	$1\frac{4}{10}$
$1\frac{1}{5}$	$1\frac{3}{4}$	$1\frac{2}{3}$	$1\frac{1}{3}$	$\frac{2}{3}$
$\frac{6}{8}$	$\frac{3}{8}$	$\frac{5}{8}$	$\frac{7}{8}$	$\frac{5}{9}$

Labsheet 1.1B

Getting Close Cards

$\frac{4}{7}$	0.5	0.75	0.6	0.9
0.125	0.375	0.875	1.5	1.75
1.125	0.2	0.8	1.33	1.67
0.33	0.67	1.875	0.1	1.9
1.1	2	1.45	1.25	1.6

Labsheet 1.1C

Getting Close Number Squares

0	0	0	0	0	0
0.5	0.5	0.5	0.5	0.5	0.5
1	1	1	1	1	1
1.5	1.5	1.5	1.5	1.5	1.5
2	2	2	2	2	2
2.5	2.5	2.5	2.5	2.5	2.5
3	3	3	3	3	3

Labsheet 2.1

Land Sections

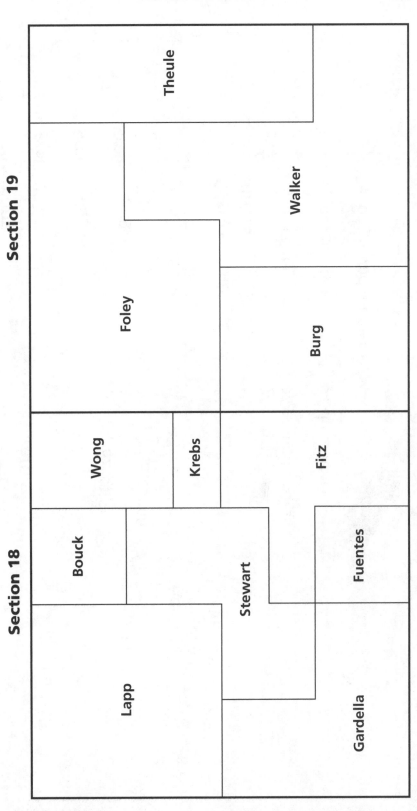

Recipe Cards

Spice Parisienne

$\frac{2}{5}$ oz ground cloves

$1\frac{1}{5}$ oz ground nutmeg

$1\frac{1}{5}$ oz ground ginger

$1\frac{1}{10}$ oz cinnamon

Betty's Fruitcake Spices

$1\frac{1}{8}$ oz cardamom

$2\frac{1}{2}$ oz allspice

$2\frac{5}{8}$ oz ground nutmeg

$\frac{5}{8}$ oz ground cloves

$4\frac{1}{4}$ oz cinnamon

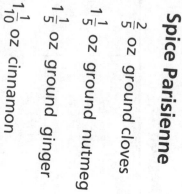

Garam Masala

$\frac{2}{3}$ oz cinnamon

$6\frac{1}{2}$ oz cardamom

$2\frac{1}{2}$ oz cumin

$\frac{1}{3}$ oz ground cloves

$\frac{2}{3}$ oz coriander

$2\frac{3}{4}$ oz black pepper

Grind all spices together with a mortar and pestle or in a coffee mill.

Labsheet 2ACE Exercise 1

Flower Garden

Marigolds		Lantana

Impatiens

Petunias

Lillies

| Begonias | Tulips | Daisies | Irises |

Labsheet 3.1

Brownie Pans

_____

Mathematical Goals

PACING: _____

_____
_____
_____
_____

Launch

_____
_____
_____
_____
_____
_____
_____

Materials

Explore

_____
_____
_____
_____
_____
_____
_____

Materials

Summarize

_____
_____
_____
_____
_____
_____

Materials

127

Glossary

A

algorithm A set of rules for performing a procedure. Mathematicians invent algorithms that are useful in many kinds of situations. Some examples of algorithms are the rules for long division or the rules for adding two fractions. The following algorithm was written by a middle-grade student:

To add two fractions, first change them to equivalent fractions with the same denominator. Then add the numerators and put the sum over the common denominator.

B

benchmark A "nice" number that can be used to estimate the size of other numbers. For work with fractions, 0, $\frac{1}{2}$, and 1 are good benchmarks. We often estimate fractions or decimals with benchmarks because it is easier to do arithmetic with them, and estimates often give enough accuracy for the situation. For example, many fractions and decimals—such as $\frac{37}{50}$, $\frac{5}{8}$, 0.43, and 0.55—can be thought of as being close to $\frac{1}{2}$. You might say $\frac{5}{8}$ is between $\frac{1}{2}$ and 1 but closer to $\frac{1}{2}$, so you can estimate $\frac{5}{8}$ to be about $\frac{1}{2}$. We also use benchmarks to help compare fractions. For example, we could say that $\frac{5}{8}$ is greater than 0.43 because $\frac{5}{8}$ is greater than $\frac{1}{2}$ and 0.43 is less than $\frac{1}{2}$.

D

denominator The number written below the line in a fraction. In the fraction $\frac{3}{4}$, 4 is the denominator. In the part-whole interpretation of fractions, the denominator shows the number of equal-sized parts into which the whole has been split.

E

equivalent fractions Fractions that are equal in value, but may have different numerators and denominators. For example, $\frac{2}{3}$ and $\frac{14}{21}$ are equivalent fractions. The shaded part of this rectangle represents both $\frac{2}{3}$ and $\frac{14}{21}$.

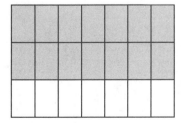

F

fact family A set of related addition-subtraction sentences or multiplication-division sentences. For example, the set of numbers, 3, 5, and 15, are part of this multiplication-division fact family:

$$3 \times 5 = 15 \qquad 5 \times 3 = 15$$
$$15 \div 5 = 3 \qquad 15 \div 3 = 5$$

If you have one fact from a family, you can use the addition-subtraction or multiplication-division relationship to write the three related facts that are also part of the family. For example with $2 + 3 = 5$, you can use the relationship between addition and subtraction to write the related number sentences $3 + 2 = 5, 5 - 3 = 2$, and $5 - 2 = 3$.

N

numerator The number written above the line in a fraction. In the fraction $\frac{5}{8}$, 5 is the numerator. When you interpret the fraction $\frac{5}{8}$ as a part of a whole, the numerator 5 tells that the fraction refers to 5 of the 8 equal parts.

R

reciprocal A factor by which you multiply a given number so that their product is 1. For example, $\frac{3}{5}$ is the reciprocal of $\frac{5}{3}$, and $\frac{5}{3}$ is the reciprocal of $\frac{3}{5}$ because $\frac{3}{5} \times \frac{5}{3} = 1$. Note that the reciprocal of $1\frac{2}{3}$ is $\frac{3}{5}$ because $1\frac{2}{3} \times \frac{3}{5} = 1$.

U

unit fraction A fraction with a numerator of 1. For example, in the unit fraction $\frac{1}{13}$, the part-whole interpretation of fractions tells us that the whole has been split into 13 equal-sized parts, and that the fraction represents the quantity of 1 of those parts.

Index

Acknowledgments

Team Credits

The people who made up the **Connected Mathematics 2** team—representing editorial, editorial services, design services, and production services—are listed below. Bold type denotes core team members.

Leora Adler, Judith Buice, Kerry Cashman, Patrick Culleton, Sheila DeFazio, Richard Heater, **Barbara Hollingdale, Jayne Holman,** Karen Holtzman, **Etta Jacobs,** Christine Lee, Carolyn Lock, Catherine Maglio, **Dotti Marshall,** Rich McMahon, Eve Melnechuk, Kristin Mingrone, Terri Mitchell, **Marsha Novak,** Irene Rubin, Donna Russo, Robin Samper, Siri Schwartzman, **Nancy Smith,** Emily Soltanoff, **Mark Tricca,** Paula Vergith, Roberta Warshaw, Helen Young

Additional Credits

Diana Bonfilio, Mairead Reddin, Michael Torocsik, nSight, Inc.

Technical Illustration

Seven Worldwide

Cover Design

tom white.images